JEAN TOURS A HOSPITAL

JEAN TOURS A HOSPITAL

DOREEN SWINBURNE

COLLINS
LONDON AND GLASGOW

This Impression 1962

PRINTED AND MADE IN GREAT BRITAIN
BY WILLIAM COLLINS SONS AND CO. LTD.
LONDON AND GLASGOW

CONTENTS

AUTHOR'S NOTE

CONDITIONS OF TRAINING

(*The passing of the National Health Act has brought about certain changes in the conditions of nursing training and employment. For those readers, or their parents, who wish to know more precisely the present conditions of training, I append this note.—D.S.*)

The accepted qualification for a nurse is State Registration. This may be gained by examination at the end of a course of training in a hospital approved as a training school by the General Nursing Council.

Candidates should be at least eighteen years old before entering general training. The first eight to twelve weeks of the course are spent in the preliminary school in charge of sister tutors. This gives both candidate and hospital authorities the opportunity to find out whether she is fitted for hospital life and work.

If considered suitable, the student nurse is then given clinical instruction and practical experience in the various wards and departments of the hospital.

She also attends courses of lectures given by the hospital physicians and surgeons.

During this time the student normally lives in a hostel or nurses' home attached to the hospital. (Although some hospital matrons are now encouraging nurses to find their own accommodation, this is not always considered suitable when the student is young and in the early years of training.) Food and laundry are provided and the student's health is supervised by the medical staff of the hospital.

Most nurses' homes provide attractive accommodation, with separate bedrooms for each nurse, common sitting-rooms, recreation rooms, often central heating, gardens and facilities for sport.

The nursing profession is one for which a student can qualify without financial assistance if necessary, as there are no fees for any part of the training course. From the day of entry to the Preliminary Training School she is given a training allowance, commencing at £299 a year and rising to £336 in the third year of training. If she is resident in accommodation provided by the hospital, she pays £128 a year for board, lodging, and the use and laundering of uniform.

Although, since the passing of the National Health Act, conditions of training have been brought very much into line in all hospitals—that is to say, the duration of training, salaries and certain emoluments are fixed—nevertheless there remain some variations between hospital and hospital with regard to the hours of duty each week and the conditions of living provided. It remains wise, therefore, to investigate and consider those differences before finally choosing a hospital for training.

Training and State Registration may be obtained in the following branches of nursing:

1. GENERAL NURSING
(Minimum course of three years in a general hospital or group of hospitals approved for complete training, or of four years in two hospitals approved for affiliated training. Under the scheme for affiliated training, it is possible to take part of the course in an approved sanatorium, orthopædic or other special hospital, while preparing for State Registration in general nursing.)

2. THE NURSING OF SICK CHILDREN
(Minimum course of three years)

3. FEVER NURSING
(Minimum course of two years)

4. MENTAL NURSING
(Minimum course of three years)

5. THE NURSING OF MENTAL DEFECTIVES
(Minimum course of three years)

The course in general nursing is regarded as the basic training, and those who take any of the special trainings are well advised to qualify in general nursing also. Those who are State registered in one branch of nursing may take a shortened course if they wish to qualify in another branch.

POST REGISTRATION TRAINING IN HOSPITAL

General trained and registered sick children's nurses may work for the certificate of the Central Midwives' Board in one year, and others may obtain this qualification in two years. Certificates are also given by the British Tuberculosis Association (one year), the Joint Examination Board of the British Orthopædic Association and the Central Council for the care of cripples (one year), and the Midland Institute of Otology (one year).

ASSISTANT NURSES

Those who find the State examination too difficult can now take a one-year course of training on simpler lines followed by one year's nursing practice under supervision, in order to become State-enrolled assistant nurses. There are training schools for assistant nurses in many parts of the country, and opportunities for interesting work after qualification are increasing.

For the State registered nurse, opportunities of employment at home and abroad are many and varied. Nurses are needed everywhere, in hospitals, health centres and in private homes; on ships and aeroplanes; in the armed services, the colonial Service and in Missionary Societies.

A qualified nurse's salary commences at £525 per annum and can rise to as much as £1,643 though it is fair to point out that this is the salary of a matron in charge of a very large teaching hospital. Few nurses reach that dizzy peak but a great many gain positions of responsibility at about £800 a year. And the trend in salaries continues to rise.

The most up-to-date information with regard to conditions and salaries may be obtained at any time from the Nursing Recruitment Service at 6 Cavendish Square, London, W.1.

During recent years the material rewards of nursing have increased out of all recognition, yet the essential reward of the work remains the same. Nursing is a great and intimate human service, and to those who can give generously to it come very rich and personal satisfactions.

CHAPTER ONE

JEAN MEETS A MATRON

JEAN stood on the doorstep of the Princess Mary's Home and pressed the bell. She heard it ring in the distance.

To-day was her half-holiday from school and she had looked forward to this visit to Norah, ever since her cousin had spent a whole day visiting *her*. It had been Norah's day off from St. Mary's Hospital and she had ended it by sitting on Jean's bed and telling her all about the patients who came in and out of the children's ward at the Hospital. Cousin Norah had promised to take her into the ward and show her some of these children; and to-day was the promised day.

The door of Princess Mary's Home opened and a trim maid ushered her over the doorstep.

"Will you come in, Miss? Nurse Brown told me you would be coming. I'll let her know that you're here."

But there was no need. There was not even time for Jean to lower herself into one of the deep chairs which stood in the entrance-hall promising comfort to whoever must wait there.

Here was Norah, looking fresher than ever in a crisp white linen apron over her sky-blue frock. Her little white cap sat on the very back of curling red hair, which Daddy mischievously said was just like Mummy's before her family had turned it grey. Of course, Norah's mother was Mummy's sister, so that explained it.

"*There* you are, Jean! I'm so glad you came early, because Matron says that I may take you all over the Hospital so long as I introduce you to her first. But you won't mind that, will you?"

Jean wasn't so sure. Matrons, she had heard, were worse than headmistresses, and everyone knew that headmistresses were usually awful, all except the one at St. Bride's, which was Jean's own school and therefore different. However, visitors can't be choosers, so: "No, of course not; I—I mean, I'd love to, thank you, Norah," said Jean, wishing that Mummy could hear her. Such politeness would surely turn her hair to red again.

Norah was flinging a short blue cape round her shoulders. It was lined with red, and two red bands crossed the white bib of her apron and buttoned beneath the cloak at the back. Jean watched, fascinated.

"Why didn't you come home in that, Norah?" she asked. "It's much prettier with your cap, than an ordinary hat and coat."

"Not allowed, my dear. We call these corridor

capes. They are really designed for speed and economy, as well as to follow tradition. They use up less time and material than a jacket and are quite warm enough for travelling to and from the Hospital even in the coldest weather—but they are *not* considered an adequate covering for long walks into town."

"Not even if it's a warm day?" asked Jean.

"Oh, it has nothing to do with warmth, my dear, it's a matter of germs."

"Germs?" cried Jean in astonishment.

"Yes, you see, we are dealing with ill people who are already fighting an army of invading germs and don't want their enemy strengthened by fresh reinforcements. So we make a point of *not* going into town and rubbing our white linen aprons up against everything and everybody. These capes are just for short jaunts—to the post-office on the corner and back again is the limit. If we want to go farther we put on long coats or change into mufti."

"*Mufti*, Norah?" laughed Jean.

"Yes, that's slang picked up from the last war, I think; anyway it only means private dress but it's quicker to say."

Norah led the way down a long parquet corridor, past doors which shut in murmuring voices, to a glass door leading on to a veranda which ran along a whole side of the building. Now the voices were clamorous. The windows of the rooms opened wide on to the veranda and girlish voices sailed unchecked across the summer air.

"We won't bother about the closed-in corridor," said Norah. "I can show you that on the way back, but we usually use the path through the gardens in this sort of weather."

"This is a *lovely* way," said Jean, in honest admiration.

She looked across the smooth lawns to the brilliant flower-beds. A high privet hedge shut off the view beyond, but the ping . . . ping of a ball against rackets, and the sound of clear voices raised in fun, told her of activity behind the screen of the privet.

"Is that your tennis club functioning over there, Norah?" she asked.

"Yes; that'll be Squiffy and Tops . . . the Nurses Squiffham and Topping to be precise. They are in training for the staff tournament. We rely on them to smash the pride out of the house-doctors; they're good too . . . Squiffy and Tops, I mean."

As she spoke they had reached the end of the gravel path, which turned directly left towards an opening in the privet hedge; but ignoring it, Norah turned to the right, following a smooth trodden path through the orchard.

"I'd no idea that the Hospital grounds were so big," said Jean in astonishment.

"Well, they aren't very, but they seem it because

somebody must have planned them carefully. Behind the tennis courts are the vegetables; the pride and delight of Robin our gardener who was once a patient. He and Matron are as one over this garden."

She looked back at the lawns and flower-beds.

"Those were laid as a special concession to Matron. Robin would far rather have gone on growing vegetables all over the gardens as he had to during the war. Rumour says that then we even kept a cow in the orchard. Well . . . here we are."

They turned a corner at the end of the long path and there stood the dark red building which had only been dimly visible through the trees. The little path from the Nurses' Home seemed to have shrunk to the size of a pygmy track in comparison with the two gravel drives which swept up to the Hospital from the road beyond.

Norah waved up at the front of the building, and following her gaze Jean saw an old woman sitting in a bath-chair on a veranda. She fluttered a large white handkerchief.

"That's Mrs. Tomkins," explained Norah, "she's been in for months, and knows nearly every nurse in the Hospital. Now that she's better she loves nothing more than to sit in the sun waving to all the nurses as they come on duty."

Jean's eyes were still strained up to the open windows. On each veranda was at least one bed, its occupant absorbing all the healing rays of the sun.

"Nothing like fresh air and sunshine to blow away the germs," exclaimed Norah.

"Those germs again, what all-important creatures they must be," laughed Jean.

"That's what *they* think, but we show them who's master once we get them in here," answered Norah.

They mounted the three wide steps of the Hospital and passed through the open doorway.

An old man sat behind a little glass window just inside the entrance.

"Afternoon, Nurse," he said cheerily through his heavy moustache, and his eyes twinkled kindly at Jean over the top of it.

"Afternoon, George," answered Norah. "Is Matron in her room?"

"She just went up five minutes ago, Nurse," he said.

Norah turned to Jean. "This way to the cloak-room; then I can leave my cloak there. It simply isn't done to go and see Matron in a cloak."

"Isn't it? Ought I to take my coat off then?"

"Oh, no, that's different. You're just a visitor, but when I go to Matron in uniform I have to be formal. To go in a cloak would be like walking into a ballroom in all your evening wraps. Here's the nurses' cloakroom."

The telephone was ringing by the main entrance

and as the door of the cloakroom swung behind them, Jean could hear George's voice answering it. "St. Mary's 'Orspital," said George.

The cloakroom was scrubbed and bare, with rows of hooks facing a row of wash-basins. Norah turned from the mirror after some careful manipulation of her cap, to see Jean standing rather fearfully on one foot, and quietly scratching the back of her leg with the other.

"You're not nervous about seeing Matron, are you?" inquired Norah.

"N-no, not really . . . that is . . . well, it's really everything. Not just Matron, but . . . actually being in a hospital . . . and the *smell*, and knowing that all sorts of awful things must be happening in this very building . . . *now*."

"Aha . . . cold feet," teased Norah, then she added seriously, "but if that is your impression of hospitals, then it's just about time you came and had a look at one. There's nothing *awful* about them at all; on the contrary, they're kind, friendly places. As for the smell; that's just a clean smell." She sniffed appreciatively. "It is one of the ways in which we out-do our enemy the germs. The heavy, sweet smell you may have noticed in the hall filters through from the theatre, but *that* is an anæsthetic which isn't terrible at all; it saves pain. It *would* be terrible if no one had discovered anæsthetics. . . . Now, any other fears?"

"No . . . I don't think so . . . but will I have to see many things . . . *nasty* things, I mean . . . like *blood*?" said Jean tentatively.

Norah's laugh echoed all round the washroom.

"You've come to the wrong place for that," she gurgled. "We don't waste such a vital fluid by spilling it about. Besides, blood isn't just something rather messy to shudder about. It is the cleanest content of our bodies and as precious as life itself. In fact it *is* life and therefore not at all disgusting."

Jean nodded. "I see," she said. "Nevertheless, I don't want to see it . . . much."

"You won't, never fear," chuckled Norah, as she led the way out of the washroom and towards the iron gates of the lift.

With a clanging of ironwork they rose to the first floor of the Hospital. Here the stone floors gave way to a smooth parquet and together Norah and Jean skidded along to a heavy white door marked "MATRON. Knock and Enter." Norah did so, and Jean crept in behind.

As they entered, a navy-blue figure, crowned in white, turned from a large desk and greeted them kindly.

"Good afternoon, Nurse," and to Jean who was hovering uncertainly, "Come right in, my dear."

"Good afternoon, Matron," answered Norah, and Jean noticed that her usual perky expression had been replaced by one of extreme mildness. In dulcet tones she continued. "Matron, here is my cousin, Jean, who has come to see the Hospital."

Jean's eyes were fixed on the face of the woman before them. Why . . . she was younger than the most popular arts mistress at school, and *quite* as good-looking! Her navy-blue dress was of a silken material and carefully tailored to her figure. Above it her cap, as white as driven snow, sat upon smooth brown hair. Her voice was soft and measured, but through the quiet answer her keen eyes twinkled up at Norah.

"And you are her appointed guide, so to start with you had better explain me and my works . . . or should I do it for you, then you can add your own comments later?" Patting a small chair beside her she turned to Jean. "Sit down here, Jean, and listen to a Matron's tale." She inclined smilingly towards Jean and continued, ignoring the girl's momentary discomfort which obviously grew less with each word.

"Now, as you probably know, I am here to look after all the patients and all the nurses, but as I teach my nurses to look after the patients, it boils down to the fact that I specialise in looking after the nurses, which *may* sound simple, but . . ." she laughed and shot a glance at Norah, ". . . that rather depends on the nurses, doesn't it?"

A little smile was hovering at the corner of Norah's mouth but the rest of her remained demure, and Jean couldn't help comparing the picture she presented with the boisterous cousin who had chased Mummy over the lawn with a live frog. "Yes, it certainly must," said Jean, remembering how Mummy had said that Norah was more of a handful than three times her weight in boys.

Matron laughed as she continued. "So here I sit with a list of rules to help me, because I really *can't* be everywhere at once, even though every nurse's Mother and Father want to know what is happening to their daughter. So, in this way, I can at least say what they are *not* doing . . . that, at any rate, is my intention and the reason for my list of rules.

"Fortunately, I have a brighter function. I arrange the holidays and days off. The hours off each day are suggested by the ward-sisters and come to me for my approval. Naturally I interview many would-be nurses and advise them as to their suitability for the profession."

Jean's eyes opened more widely than ever.

"Surely they wouldn't *want* to be a nurse unless they knew that they would like it," she suggested.

"But you see," explained Matron, "I have to con-sider whether the *patients* will like *them*, haven't I? . . . And then, of course, a girl may *think* that she would like to nurse and discover when time and money has been spent on preliminary training that she is particularly unsuited. If possible I like to prevent such a waste."

"Yes, of course," said Jean, quite forgetting to be nervous, "but *how* can you tell beforehand?"

"I give every would-be probationer a list of simple questions with her application form. I advise her to answer them as honestly as she can after careful thought. Then when she comes for her interview we discuss the answers."

Matron opened a drawer in her desk and took out a form which she handed to Jean who read:

Are you easily tired?
Can you take long walks?
Do you like the people that you meet in buses?
Do you get upset over trifles?
Do disappointments dishearten you?
Do you show disappointment?
Have you a sense of humour?
Do you like parties?
Have you ever seen any one in pain?
. . . . How did it affect you?
Do you find examinations difficult?

Jean was just about to hand the form back again when she hesitated. "May I . . .?" she began.

"Yes, do keep it, if you are interested," said Matron, and Jean pushed the form in her pocket, trying not to feel Norah smiling at her.

"But that isn't *all* you do, Matron," pressed Norah, "what about the housekeeping?"

"Yes, but that," said Matron, "is where I am fortunate in having a splendid Home Sister and Hospital Housekeeper. Certainly they come to me with all the queries so I am in a sense in charge of them too, but luckily for me they are both perfectly capable and I can safely present their books to the Hospital Committee. Of course, in some smaller Hospitals the matron has to act as Housekeeper, Home Sister and Sister Tutor to her nurses, but in a Hospital as large as this, that wouldn't be possible. There are so many other calls on one's time and energy."

"Is this considered a large hospital then?" asked Jean.

"Well," said Matron, "it has two hundred beds. It could not be a training school for nurses unless it had at least one hundred and fifty. But these numbers are small compared with the thousand or more beds of the medical training schools.

"Such large hospitals may not always contain their beds within the one set of walls. Sometimes they are several hospitals now bound together within a group. As well as curing the patients, these hospitals have also to teach and train medical students to be doctors. The medical school is an integral and important part of the hospital. And, of course such large hospitals have, too, a training school for nurses; so that there are two sets of students working side by side on the wards. It has its drawbacks. You see, if the medical students are given certain tests or treatments to perform, then the student nurse's experience of that particular procedure will, to some extent, be limited. It is up to those who plan her training to see that it is not too limited."

As Matron spoke Jean thought she looked older, and even rather worn—then the laughter came back into her voice and the twinkle to her eye as she said, "But you don't want to hear about we old people on top—you run along with Nurse and see what all the young ones are doing.

"Don't let her miss a thing, Nurse. If she wants to know of our work she must see the bad with the good."

On rising, Jean's eye caught sight of a silver-framed portrait on the wall facing Matron's desk. The figure might have been anybody's Grandmother, with high neck, shawl, and a little mob cap. But there was something about that face which caught her attention; something so calm, yet so strong.

"Is . . . is that . . .?" faltered Jean, because it might be impertinent but she *must* know. Matron followed her glance and smiled. She, too, kept her glance on the portrait as she answered.

"Yes, that is the leader of us all—Miss Florence Nightingale. Many years ago when hospitals were places of evil smell and almost inevitable death; when doctors were progressing in skill yet being discouraged by the low standard of nursing which accompanied their work . . . Miss Florence Nightingale left a comfortable home to devote her life to nursing. Her wonderful enthusiasm encouraged other women to do the same, so that eventually the care of the sick passed from the hands of slovenly ' watchers,' as they were called, into the hands of women who considered their work to be a vocation and were therefore ready to submerge themselves in it. Now, of course, we don't demand such a high standard of sacrifice. Nursing is gradually taking its place among the foremost of the careers for educated women. Therefore it must leave room for the wide interests of an educated girl. We have still a long way to go in that direction but with the enthusiasm of the right leaders we may yet take our place as graduates besides . . . say, doctors, lawyers, and clergymen." Matron's voice had grown deep and she spoke the words as though she had recited them before. Then, turning lightly away, she added. "We must always remember that the woman who started it all was Florence Nightingale . . . she's worth a silver frame, don't you think?"

"Yes, indeed," said Jean with feeling, as they moved towards the door.

"You must come and tell me what you think of

our Hospital when you have seen it all and sorted it over in your mind . . . will you?"

"Yes, thank you, Matron, I'd like to," said Jean, as she followed Norah through the open door, leaving Matron smiling at them from the doorway.

CHAPTER TWO

THE CHILDREN'S WARD

"You'll love St. Anne's ward," said Norah as they approached another heavy, white door. "Listen a moment."

Through the door came the muffled hum of many voices. Young voices raised in laughter, anger, and appeal.

"Now," said Norah as she pushed open the door, "more or less sound proof, you see."

Jean just gasped. There wasn't much point in saying anything as it could never have been heard above the wave of strident voices which met them with the force of a tornado. As they entered, the sounds were suspended for a moment, only to gather new force in one triumphant chant.

"Nursey."

"Nu-ur-se."

"Nurse, nurse, nurse."

"Nu-ur-ur-ur-se."

Norah was laughing and waving to the active little figures in their cots.

"I can see you, Jimmy Thomas," she laughed.

"And where is Mary-Jane? *There* she is. I'm coming, Mary-Jane." And Norah sped towards a tiny blue figure with tumbling red curls who had struggled in vain to climb her cot rails. She had just decided to burst into tears when Norah saw her . . . and immediately her mouth stretched from the round O of a howl to a broad smile of welcome. Small and large blue figures merged and two heads of red curls tumbled together. Norah's laugh was punctuated with squeaks of delight from Mary-Jane.

Jean could feel the candid gaze of a dozen pairs of eyes. She hardly dared to look around. It seemed silly to be so nervous of small children, but she was discovering for the first time that there is no judgment so telling as that of a *very* young child. She rather wished that Norah had not left her quite so soon.

It was as she was allowing her gaze to slide back again to Norah that she found Tommy Tucker. There he was, lying flat on his back, with both legs encased in plaster of paris and raised on to a large pillow. Tommy was contentedly sucking the legs of a toy soldier. He was just about to tackle its head when it fell with a tinkling sound to the floor.

Tommy rolled an eye at Jean and opened his mouth to yell. He changed his mind as she stepped forward to pick up the toy.

"That's mine," said a voice from the next cot.

Jean turned to see a little face topped with black hair.

"I gave it to him—but he sucks it," explained the same little voice as he held out his hand for the toy.

There came a threatening gurgle from the depths of Tommy Tucker. Once more his mouth was opening and his chest expanding with his anger.

Jean was looking uncertainly from one to the other when Norah came to her rescue with another young woman in a darker blue frock.

"Jean, here is Sister who looks after all these children," announced Norah. "Sister, this is my cousin Jean."

At that moment Tommy Tucker expelled all the air from his lungs in one huge roar.

"*Tommy Tucker!*" said Sister reprovingly. "What a horrible noise."

The little boy stopped in the middle of a shuddering breath and gazed at her solemnly out of clear, blue eyes. "I may do it again," he seemed to say.

"And not even a single tear," went on Sister. "Just a naughty, bad-tempered boy." But her eyes were smiling as she bent over the cot and raised the little fellow in her arms. Jean was amazed to see the plastered legs come up in a fixed position. But neither Tommy nor Sister seemed aware of anything unusual. He clasped her tightly round the neck and, laughing, buried his face there. Norah busily straightened the empty cot.

"Doesn't it hurt him?" asked Jean.

"Not a bit, does it, Tommy darling?" said Sister, as she gently lowered her precious burden into the cot and fixed the large pillow under his stiff legs. "He didn't like it so much when he first had the plaster put on, but small children soon get used to new conditions. Within a day he was playing as happily with his hands as though he had never learned to use his feet."

"What did he do to himself? Was it an accident?" questioned Jean anxiously.

"No, not exactly. He was born with slightly crooked hips," explained Sister, "and although he didn't seem very crippled as a small baby, the deformity began to show as he was learning to walk. So now he has had them straightened. He just went to sleep by blowing up a large balloon filled with a funny smelling gas. Sometimes for very young children we use some stuff that smells like eau-de-cologne . . . it's really an anæsthetic."

"Oh, yes; I've smelt it," cried Jean excitedly. "I smelt it in the hall as I came in."

"Yes, you probably did," Sister agreed. "The whole place smells of it sometimes when the theatre has been very busy. Then when Tommy was fast asleep and couldn't feel a thing, the doctor straightened the bones of his hip joints and put his legs and hips into plaster. Now he can't move them until the bones are set in the right way, and Doctor removes the plaster."

"Will he ever be able to walk properly?"

"Oh yes. When the plaster first comes off, his legs will feel rather weak because they haven't been used for so long. But we will rub—or massage—them carefully and then teach him to exercise them, so that in a week or so he will be using them properly. Years ago, before bone surgery was understood, he would have had to remain a cripple for life."

Tommy had discovered nothing very interesting in his audience and was happily playing with a squeaking bear that Sister had given him.

"He doesn't seem to mind at all," said Jean as they moved away.

There were twelve cots in the ward and they stood in two rows facing the french windows.

"These," said Sister, pointing to the row against the inside wall, "are the over-three-years-old . . . and here," she led the way to the front row down the middle of the ward, "are our six tiny ones. Aren't they beautiful?"

Each of these cots stood in its own glass cubicle, which contained also a tiny white locker and stool. Three of the occupants were making as brazened overtures to Sister as the confinement of their reins would allow. "We have to tie the little ones in," explained Sister, "or they'd climb over the sides and break their necks."

In another two cots were a large and small recumbent figure. The sixth cubicle was screened with curtains.

"Is *that* one only three years old?" asked Jean, nodding towards the larger figure.

Sister shook her head sadly. "No, but she has been so very ill and isn't well enough yet to go with the noisy ones in the back row. It is easier to nurse the more severely ill patients in a cubicle because we can shelter them with curtains if they need attention. Also there's less chance of infection."

"What infection?" asked Jean.

"Anything that's going. You see, there are always harmful germs everywhere, but most of us are able to fight them because we have been used to them for so long . . . especially when they are in our home atmosphere. We may not be able to fight the germs from other people's homes in the same way.

"As you grow older you should be able to cope with more and more germs. But very small children are only used to the ones in their own homes, so, when it becomes necessary to take them away and put them in a room with other children, we have to take special care. That is why we always put the little ones into cubicles. Then we wear these masks for nursing them so that we shall not infect them."

J.T.H.   B

Sister opened a metal box and showed Jean a small white mask.

"To cover nose and mouth. The tape ties round your head," she explained.

"I see," said Jean, "but what about the older children?"

"They are not so easily affected," Sister explained. "Most of them go to school, and the ones that don't have already started to play with other children. Of course they *do* succumb to the invasion of germs. Every mother knows that she may have to face a run of measles, chicken-pox, or mumps with her four-to-ten-years-old, but at such an age a child can more easily fight the invasion. We prefer to put off the battle till then, as a very young baby has other trials such as teething, and taking the first solid food."

"And why did you say the big child is here?" pressed Jean, looking again towards the large, recumbent figure in the cubicle.

"Because in her delicate state of health she, too, is likely to become a victim of any passing germ. We take care in other ways, of course, by giving cod-liver-oil and vitamin tablets, but the cubicles are an *excellent* precaution. Come and peep at Jennifer. She's sleeping now and we needn't disturb her."

Sister moved towards the cubicle and Jean tiptoed behind.

"She's *lovely*," she breathed.

"Yes, isn't she?" Sister agreed.

They looked down upon the slight figure in the cot. Fair, silken hair strayed across the pillow. The face beneath it was flushed in sleep. One slim hand curled beneath her chin and the other lay, palm uppermost, upon the pillow.

"She's going to be better now," said Sister.

"Oh, *good*." Jean couldn't have explained why she was so thankful. Less than five minutes ago she had never seen this sleeping child, yet now everything else was blotted out by the one great need for Jennifer's recovery. "What was it?" she asked.

"Acute rheumatism," answered Sister, "and it affected her heart."

"I thought only old people had rheumatism," remarked Jean.

Sister sighed. "Unfortunately that isn't true. The saddest cases of rheumatism occur in childhood, because though it may not appear to be serious at the time, yet the effect may be severe in the future. Fortunately we have discovered all this. Now we have a far greater respect for the ' growing pains ' which our ancestors dismissed so airily. We know now that these are usually a form of rheumatism and we can treat them far more carefully than appears necessary and so save a lot of future trouble."

"Did Jennifer only have ' growing pains ' though?" asked Jean.

"She probably did in the first place, but didn't tell her mother so that nobody knew about them. Then when she came in to us the main trouble couldn't be averted. However, she was such a good child and did everything to help us to get her better . . . so in a few months she'll be romping with the best of them."

Jean showed her surprise. "Will it take as long as that?" she asked.

"It should do," said Sister firmly. "But Jennifer won't want it to. In a week or so she will be asking to run about and play, and that is when she will need such care. If she is allowed to have her own way, her heart may not be able to stand the strain she will impose upon it. It isn't easy to keep a child like that inactive, when she feels quite well . . . but *rest* she must; and in that lies the whole secret for the treatment of *acute* rheumatism—especially in the very young.

"You see it's really the *heart* that you are helping. This poor overworked organ is often the first to be affected, and it *does* deserve every possible care.

"Think of it. Sixty to eighty times per minute your heart pumps blood round your body. Whether you are sleeping or waking it never ceases. Then think of the number of minutes in an hour . . . a day . . . a week . . . a year . . . a *lifetime*. Yet your heart may never stop.

"*You* say that you are tired . . . and go to bed.

But your heart has to go on working. The only relief it ever gets is when you are asleep; then it needn't beat quite so quickly, although, of course, it dare not stop even then. We should all remember that before we run upstairs two at a time . . . just for fun. It isn't much fun for your poor old heart as it thumps its protest in your ears."

"Good gracious," gasped Jean, "I hadn't thought of that. How can it manage to keep going?"

Sister laughed. "Well, it is pretty well made to stand a fair strain, and so it is up to us not to take liberties. Jennifer knows all about that now. Doctor explained it to her so that she understands why we insist on feeding her when she would like to feed herself. Also, illness isn't so worrying if the patient can see how she will get better."

Jean nodded thoughtfully. "Yes," she agreed. "I used to think that illness was frightening, but here . . . it seems so . . . so *ordinary*. They are all quite happy; and the *noise* when we came in . . . a good job they've stopped now for Jennifer's sake, or they might . . ." she broke off.

Sister was laughing. "Listen again, Jean," she urged.

"B-but . . . they *haven't* stopped at all," stammered Jean, flabbergasted.

"No, they certainly haven't and they won't until six o'clock to-night or a little after, but when you've been amongst it for a while . . . well, you just don't notice it," explained Sister laughingly.

"But *won't* they waken Jennifer?" Jean insisted.

"No, children are very much like animals. They can sleep through any noise so long as it is a *familiar* noise. As soon as a dog hears anything strange in the noises around him, or senses anything new in the silence, he wakes. Babies and young children are like that, too, although, perhaps, to a lesser extent. We pamper ourselves to require silence for sleeping and it is really a great pity. . . . All *right*, Johnny White, I'll pick up your elephant *this* time, but not *once* more in the next five minutes."

Sister moved forward to a little two-year-old who had thrown down his elephant in a last desperate effort to attract her attention. Now he laughed delightedly as she returned it to him with one hand and tickled him with the other. "Tea," he said through his laughter, "Johnny wants his tea."

"Very well, he shall have it in just a few minutes. Look, here's Nurse to get you ready for it." Sister left him in the hands of a young probationer who had been working her way down the row tying on bibs and adjusting tiny tables on to the cots.

Johnny White was breathless with anticipation as she tied the bib round his neck. Six more pairs of baby eyes were roving between the young nurse and the kitchen door. *Food* was in the offing . . . a serious business. Much more serious to hungry youngsters than teddy-bears and toy elephants. The older children in the back row were already manipulating their own small tables. Most of them had graduated from bibs to table-napkins with which they carefully covered the sheets.

"This is the ceremonial meal of the day," explained Sister. "It is also the last. Only the children over six years old have some milk and biscuits later. Perhaps you would like to know what they have. It varies a little with the age of the child."

But Jean's eyes were fixed on a little mite—surely only one year old—who was sucking the last scrap of butter and sugar off a piece of crusty bread. What remained was rapidly being reduced to pulp.

Sister followed her gaze. "Yes, the little ones always have a crust or rusk buttered and covered with brown sugar. It helps their gums and tickles up their appetites. Look . . . he's spotted his bread and milk."

The last remnant of crust was discarded over the cot rails with his forgotten toys as the baby saw the nurse approaching with a china mug and spoon balanced on a plate. His little mouth sucked readily even before she had time to deposit the first spoonful. Then as he received it, his cheeks bulged. Milk appeared round the corners of his mouth . . . and not a word was spoken till the nurse replaced the spoon on to the plate. Then he took a deep, satisfied breath . . . and belched.

Fascinated, Jean approached him. He threw her one disinterested glance and turned his attention to the kitchen door again.

"He's waiting for his mashed banana," said Sister. "Our little ones always have a ripe banana after it has been rubbed through a hair sieve and a little brown sugar added. The older children enjoy a fresh fruit salad. We make a thin syrup from brown sugar and water and add it to the freshly cut fruit. When this has stood for an hour or so in a cool place the juices are well mixed and the salad is delicious. For some children we add cream to this."

"Do they *all* have bread and milk?" inquired Jean anxiously, because she had never liked it very much, but had softened since seeing the baby's obvious enjoyment.

"Oh no, not after they are four or five, unless they have had their tonsils out. The older ones have bread and butter and bread and jam. . . . Then the fruit salad, occasionally with ice-cream. And last of all, because they aren't an important food, cakes and biscuits."

"And tea to drink?"

"No, never. They all have half a pint of milk, although the little ones have some of it in their bread and milk and drink the remainder after-

wards. . . . Now, come and see our special exhibit."
She led the way towards the curtained cubicle, with
Jean following nervously behind.

Perhaps, in spite of all the other cheeriness . . .
this might be something *awful*.

"This is where we shall find your cousin, I
expect," said Sister. "I saw her sneaking off as we
went to Jennifer. She never can resist tiny babies,
can she?

"This little girl is only two months old and had
quite a serious operation last night. We were worried
for a time . . . but you shall see."

Only the two sides of the cubicle which could be
overlooked by the other children were screened, so
that the light and air could enter from two sides.
The tiny sick-room was by no means close or confined.

And here was Norah. Norah with the impudence
gone from her face and in its place, not the meekness
of the girl who had interviewed her Matron, but the
beautiful compassion of a grown woman . . . a
mother. For we are all mothers as we look upon a
child so helpless as this.

The baby lay between two pillows . . . small
pillows, but her toes didn't reach beyond their
margin. She lay still . . . yet not completely so.
Swiftly and quietly the shawl upon her tiny chest
rose and fell; and rose and fell again.

"Doing marvellously," said Sister into Norah's ear. "How much has she had?"

They turned towards a stand which stood beside the cot. Norah lifted a piece of cotton wool from the bulky object which hung at the top of it. "Just over two ounces, so far," she announced.

Jean, looking over her shoulder, could see a glass flask with silver fittings. It was half-filled with a deep crimson fluid which reflected warmly in the silver.

"Pretty against that background," she thought and asked aloud. "What is she having, and how does she get it from the flask?"

Norah smiled kindly at her as she answered. "Don't faint, will you, Jean? The fluid in the flask is pure blood . . . and it is giving this baby a second chance to live."

Then Jean noticed the slender rubber tube which ran down from the flask to the cot and was lost among the folds of the shawl.

She had just grasped the amazing truth when she heard Sister saying, "What a difference in just an hour or so. This morning this little mite was dry and white . . . and shrunken. Now look at her."

Jean saw the little sleeping face, smooth in its repose. Under the fine skin a soft pink flush was spreading. Life was flowing into the tiny body, and as she grasped the wonderful significance of

this fact Jean felt a desire to cry . . . or laugh . . .
or do *something*. So she walked away.

"You didn't *mind* did you?" queried Norah
anxiously as they left the ward.

"*Mind!*" returned Jean. "No, I'm *glad*."

CHAPTER THREE

A PEEP BEHIND THE SCENES

"I THINK I'll take you to the medical wards," said Norah as she led the way towards the lift. "The surgicals will be so busy to-day. It's their main operating afternoon and they won't welcome visitors. Besides, you've seen enough surgery in St. Anne's. Our medical unit is called Mercy and we have male and female wards there, so you will get a pretty good idea of any general hospital ward from them.

"Sister's a dear, too. She trained in France during the last war and has the Royal Red Cross ribbon, which is considered pretty marvellous. Not many nurses or even matrons have it."

Norah swung open the lift doors and together they descended to the ground-floor.

By now Jean was thoroughly interested in anything that this tour might hold in store for her. All fear had gone. And then she entered Mercy corridor.

As the heavy door swung behind them it shut out normality. They had entered a new world . . . of coughs, calls, and vaguely murmuring voices.

In the distance a hollow voice was calling, "Nurse!", and then more urgently, "*Nurse!*"

"I'm coming, Gran!" The answer was young and clear and matter-of-fact. There came the sound of clattering enamel followed by a pair of hurrying footsteps.

Jean's heart sank into her boots. This evidently was *not* like St. Anne's ward. Oh, well . . . it was too late to turn back so she followed Norah who was making for the first door.

"This is the kitchen," announced Norah proudly.

Jean looked round at the scrubbed dresser, the rather dingy sink with its scarred draining boards; at the gas-stove whose polished taps vainly tried to deny the cracked enamel plate beneath them.

"Oh, is it?" she said flatly, but Norah didn't hear. She was bounding towards a figure that had appeared in the doorway.

"Oh *Tibbs*," she cried, "when did you get here?"

"I got here this morning," replied Tibbs dourly. "I *got* here because I was *sent*; and being a good girl I *came*. In other words . . . I'm here under protest."

Jean felt sympathetically drawn towards Nurse Tibbitts as she was introduced.

"I can understand your not wanting to be here," she agreed. "Of course, I haven't seen the wards yet, but this . . ." she glanced round, ". . . does seem a bit depressing."

Tibbs stared, and then as she laughed heartily, Norah joined her. Jean looked from one to the other inquiringly.

"There's nothing wrong with Mercy ward," explained Tibbs obligingly. "It's just that I didn't want to leave the maternity." She exchanged a sheepish glance with Norah, as she continued. "You see, on maternity you can always see the results of your work, and besides . . . it's more *social*."

"And there you have the explanation in a nutshell," interrupted Norah. "Perhaps I should explain that Tibbs is to be congratulated on her recent engagement to Dr. Simon Field, our resident obstetric surgeon . . . *obstetric* is only to do with maternity. Hence her reluctance to leave his ward."

"Yes," nodded Tibbs happily, as Jean stammered her congratulations. "*Mercy* ward is all right. We loved it, didn't we, Brownie?" She turned to Norah. "Do you remember our first night-duty together? This was the ward we staged it on. You were a raw recruit and I wasn't much better, although I *did* know how to make a Queen's pudding . . ."

Norah staggered to the nearest chair and clung to it, shaking with mirth. Between their laughter they explained to Jean.

"Saturday night . . . junior pro cooks the meal

. . . Queen's pudding . . . ha-ha . . . ha-ha-ha . . . she hadn't any currants . . . there she was . . . picking them out of three stale buns!"

At last all three sobered down.

"But *didn't* we have fun? Do you remember the mice? Three little mice called Anna, Hannah, and Harriet who used to come and sit by the bin as we had our early morning tea," reminded Norah. "And *look*, there's the mark on the dresser where you let the iron burn through for a solid hour."

They leapt with one accord towards the dresser. "D'you remember how frightened we were? Spent the rest of the night scrubbing and scraping, and then in the morning we had to show the great charred cavity. Didn't *say* much, did she?"

And so they continued. "D'you remember . . .?"

This kitchen was loved . . . and remembered.

"I suppose it *is* a bit threadbare, though," said Tibbs glancing round. "But within the next year or so it will be fitted out with metal sinks and all the other paraphernalia that the modern nurse seems to think necessary to her work." She sniffed dubiously.

"Now *Tibbs*," chided Norah, "don't be uppish. Because you've finished your training and are about to leave the profession in clouds of glory, don't grudge us our paths of progress. We won't be any the less nurses just because our new tools are sleek and labour-saving."

She turned to Jean. "I'll show you the duty-room," she said, "and then you'll know what I mean. The Hospital is being renovated by degrees, and they have started with the most important parts. The main kitchens are already done, but these ward kitchens are really only used for boiling an egg, making toast, and washing dishes. All the main cooking is done upstairs. I'll show you that afterwards. But they *have* done the duty-rooms which are attached to each ward and are used for preparing the dressing trolleys and storing the more delicate instruments of our trade. They are more important than kitchens."

"*Are* they?" Jean was surprised. "I thought that anything to do with food . . ."

". . . *must* be clean," finished off Norah. "Of course, but there's nothing dirty in here." Jean, looking round at the scrubbed, old wood-work, had to agree, as Norah continued. "But whereas food is perfectly wholesome so long as it is fresh and clean, *dressing trolleys* and anything to do with post-operative treatment have to be *completely germ free.* You can *eat* your peck of dirt without dying, but you can't absorb it through a wound, so *this* is how we keep our apparatus."

She led the way from the ward-kitchen towards a room across the corridor, nearly colliding with a stout woman in a large green overall.

"Nurse Brown!" cried the large one.

"*Hallo*, Moll," greeted Norah. "How's your leg?"

"There's rain acomin' Nurse, rain acomin'. It's painin' me somethink awful."

"Oh, I *am* sorry, Moll," said Norah sympathetically. "Jean, this is Molly of Mercy ward. She's in charge of all the ward-cleaning. Shows us *how*, don't you, Moll? She had an accident to her leg last year and it always hurts her when there's rain about."

"Bloomin' barometer, that's me," agreed Moll ruefully.

"I thought you said that the *nurses* have to clean the wards," remarked Jean as Moll left them.

"They do a lot of it," returned Norah. "But the ward-cleaner attends to all the floors, corridors, mats, grates, and the kitchen; that leaves us the ward dusting. Beds and lockers, etc.; and quite enough too."

"It doesn't sound nearly as much as I thought nurses did, though," insisted Jean.

"You sound like one of the group of people who thought we ought to go on sweeping the wards," laughed Norah. "Fortunately that's a fading custom and, believe me, it leaves us quite a lot to do.

"Most wards contain at least twelve or fifteen beds, of which the two day ward-nurses usually make half when they come on duty in the morning. The other half are made by the night-nurses.

"Then each day-nurse takes a side of the ward for cleaning. Every bed has been pulled away from the wall as it is made, and the floor has been swept by the ward-cleaner. So first of all we rush down the backs of the beds with a duster; *using* it, of course. Then back go the beds and the rest of the ward furniture is dusted and sometimes polished. After that we put on the counterpanes and the ward starts to look shipshape.

"Then the junior of the two nurses does the wet-dusting, that is washing and dusting the lockers and cleaning the doctors' sink. During that time the senior nurse arranges the flowers—which often takes a good half-hour, especially after visiting day —and takes all the patients' temperatures. That should *all* be done in about an hour, and somewhere or other between, or after, there are such odd jobs as sorting the laundry and dispensary.

"So you see, the day *must* come when even the dusting will be done by ward-maids, because as medical progress develops there are added to our already overburdened programmes many extra treatments—or preparations for treatment—which have to be done by the ward-nurse in time for the doctor's round."

"Doesn't Sister do any of that?" asked Jean.

"Not the cleaning, but she sometimes helps with the treatments *when* she's got time."

"Why, what is *she* doing all the time?"

Norah laughed. "You might well ask, but it would be easier to tell you what she *doesn't* do. You see, the ward-sister is responsible for everything that ever happens in the ward, from the well-being of the patients to the emptying of the pig-buckets. She can't *do* it all, of course, but she must see that it *is* all done. And if anything goes wrong at any time, it is no good for her to say, 'Please, I wasn't on duty.' She has to make arrangements that nothing *can* go wrong when she is not on duty. And then we wonder why they are sometimes irritable!"

"But does she just walk around all the time, watching what you are all doing?"

Norah laughed delightedly. "I'd just love them to hear you ask that.

"Indeed they don't. Don't forget there *are* such things as anxious relatives, worried patients, zealous doctors, awkward probationers, high-handed staff-nurses, forms to be filled in, treatments ordered, stores, linen, equipment, Matron, inquiries, inquiries, and ever more inquiries! . . . All right, I'll explain, though you must realise that the work of the nurses and sisters may not be quite the same in every hospital. Some are more modern than others, but this is a fair example.

"When Sister first comes on duty she is usually surrounded by forms and charts to be completed and signed. They are for the Hospital records. Then, having taken the report from the night-nurse, she hands it over to the day-nurses with instructions for treatments, admissions, discharges, and operations for the day. Most sisters then glance over the laundry and dispensary sheets, order stores of food and cleaning material for the day.

"Then, if she's lucky, Sister starts on a round of the patients, asking them how they feel and straightening out their problems for them. More often than not this is disturbed or postponed by telephone inquiries from anxious relatives, or a hurried visit from some young doctor who has to spend the rest of the morning in the Out-Patient Department, and wants to see his in-patients first—*or* perhaps there will come a new patient or two to be admitted (more explanations!)—*or* maybe a patient or two for discharge, in which case Sister usually takes them downstairs to the front door and sends them on their way. *Or* it may be an operating morning and she will take the cases to the theatre—*or*, as so often happens, several of these things coincide and, to add to her joys, two of Sister's nurses are booked for a morning lecture, which they *must* attend.

"Now perhaps that gives you a rough idea. You just *can't* say what a sister is doing, or has done; she copes with every little emergency, giving to it whatever it demands at the time.

"Then, one fine morning, when the fates are not calling her in ten different directions, she decides

to have a little nose around. And what she finds!
Somebody has thrown a large crust into the pig-
bucket . . . why wasn't it used up? She distinctly
remembers putting twelve new needles in the needle-
jar and now there are only seven . . . where are
the other five?

"Nurses shake solemn heads and declare with
soulful agony that there were only seven when
they came to the ward.

"' But I ordered twelve . . . I *had* twelve . . . I
gave them to somebody to put in the jar . . . *who*
did I give them to?' More doleful headshakes."

Norah laughed gaily. "Somehow we live through
those mornings and *don't* we just love talking about
them afterwards. It's the spice of life . . . a week
or so later."

"But aren't the sisters awfully unpopular?" asked
Jean. "Having to bully like that, I mean."

"Oh no. If they are for a time they manage to
live through it. After all, they have their own
satellites, with whom they can discuss our short-
comings as complacently as we discuss theirs.
But . . ." she was serious for a moment ". . . all
this is more *wearing* than it should be, because I think
they are responsible for too much. Think how nice
it would be for them to have fewer patients to watch
over and more nurses to teach. And the housekeeping part . . . there *could* be a sort of floor
housekeeper to superintend all stores, linen, and

cleaning. That is easily enough for one person to manage. However . . . time will come." They had been talking in the doorway of a large tiled room. Now Jean looked round it.

"This is where we clean and keep our instruments and prepare the trays and trolleys for dressings and other treatments," announced Norah.

Jean sniffed. Perhaps the heavy tang in the air was from the jars of coloured fluid which glittered from glass shelves.

The whole room shone, and the little colour that it contained was reflected again and again in the shining glass, the chromium, and tiles with which it was fitted.

"This duty-room is washed and polished every day," said Norah.

"What a long job," returned Jean. "It must take someone all day."

"Oh no it doesn't. You see it is never allowed to get dirty and all this glass and chromium only needs a wipe with a soapy cloth, and a polish with a dry one. It doesn't take more than fifteen minutes to do the lot."

Jean looked surprised until Norah explained.

"Notice that everything is tucked away in glass jars with fitting lids, or into glass cabinets, so that dust can only settle lightly on the smooth surfaces. All the cupboards and jars are turned out once a week and the lotion replaced by fresh."

Jean approached a row of shining jars in which the lotions were shimmering blue, pink and mauve.

"They are a mild antiseptic lotion," replied Norah. "All those little things inside them—rubber tubing —safety-pins—glass rods and needles, are things we need at any time of the day or night. This is a medical ward, of course, so there aren't as many here as there are in any of the surgical duty-rooms. The surgical wards specialise in operations, you see, while we only operate when medical treatment has failed to give as good results as we expect. These small implements are used in treating and dressing most wounds, and therefore they have to be *germ-free*. If we left them open to the air it would mean that every time we needed them they would have to be boiled to destroy the germs which would be on them. So for convenience, we boil a lot at a time—usually on a Sunday—and put them into an antiseptic lotion so that no germs can enter and remain alive. Then, as they are wanted, we can lift them out of the lotion with a pair of forceps, knowing that they are quite fit to go near a wound."

"But, how do you touch a wound to dress it, without putting germs into it, if germs are everywhere?"

"That's a bit difficult to explain without showing you, but *everything* on the dressing-trolley has been boiled or baked and handled with a long pair of forceps which have stood in disinfectant. Then all these things are covered over with more baked towels, so that everything beneath the towels is aseptic—or germ free—as it goes to the patient. Then as the old dressing is removed from the wound, whoever is to touch the wound scrubs her hands and arms for three minutes under running water and then rinses them in an antiseptic lotion. Even then she cleans the wound and applies the dressing with sterile forceps, just as you eat your food with a knife and fork . . . and, of course, the wound is surrounded by baked towels so that the whole process really *is* germ free."

Jean shuddered. " *Ugh*, it must hurt!"

Norah laughed. "Honestly . . . it hardly ever does. Of course it would be silly to say that no dressing ever hurts, but most of them are just clean incisions which heal within a week after operation, and such patients quite look forward to having their dressings done. They have their nurse to themselves for a few minutes, so they can chat without wasting her time, which is always so precious. Oh . . . I'd better show you this . . . it's what we do all the boiling in; it's a steriliser."

Norah turned to a shining silver tank against the wall. It was *much* bigger than the tank in the bathroom cupboard at home and it stood fairly close to the ground, so that a grown girl could comfortably lift the lid by the wooden handle and look down into it. Norah did so, and Jean, peering into its steaming depths saw twenty or more enamel bowls and dishes of every size. Each fitted snugly into the next.

"All sterile," announced Norah. Then she turned to another handle which lifted a smaller lid, and, looking in, Jean saw the glint of silver in the steam.

"Those are instruments," explained Norah, "and this thing that looks like a tea urn is for boiling water so that we shall always have some ready to add to the lotions if we want it. You just turn on this tap. We are going to have them in the kitchens, too, when they are modernised."

"For making tea?" asked Jean.

"That's right, no more heavy kettles. . . . Well, if it isn't Mrs. Atkins!" Norah looked delightedly at the newcomer in the doorway.

Mrs. Atkins generously overflowed from a pale-green kimono on which sunflowers were chased by large blue butterflies.

"Nurse *Brown*, dear! I thought I heard your voice as I was coming along to the kitchen for another piece of bread for Granny Tomkins. She *do* get that hungry. I thought, that's *our* Nurse Brown, that is, and no other . . . and *there* you was." Mrs. Atkins beamed upon Norah. "As bonny as ever, too, as I can see with my two eyes," and she transferred the beam to Jean.

"Mrs. Atkins has been with us for a long time

now," Norah explained to Jean. "She's one of our prize specimens."

"Yes, and wouldn't be here at all if it wasn't for someone I could mention," interrupted Mrs. Atkins, pursing her lips and nodding at Norah. She turned to Jean. "Right down angel she is. Brought me back from the dark valley . . . bless her . . . I shan't never forget . . ." Mrs. Atkins was fighting down her tears.

Norah remained unembarrassed. She was smiling kindly as she said, "What a blessing for Mercy ward that you decided to come though, Mrs. Atkins." And to Jean. "She's our right hand. She makes out the supper list (hot milks, cold milks, and bovrils) and *insists* on fetching and carrying extra bread from the kitchen. I don't know what Sister would say if she knew, but she *will* do it, the bad lass."

"Sister wouldn't say nothing to a great strong woman like me lifting a hand occasionally for them what's been so kind. Nothing wrong with me now; I'm going home Tuesday."

"That *is* good news," said Norah. "And you're really feeling better?"

"Never felt better in my life. It's that diet. I'm keeping it up, strict, when I get home."

"Mind you do then," laughed Norah.

"*And what is Mrs. Atkins doing out here?*" The voice was deep and rich.

"Oh, Sister, it's my fault," gasped Norah as she swung round to the dark-blue figure in the doorway. "She heard my voice and came along to see."

But Sister's eyes were warm behind the closed countenance.

"Did Mrs. Atkins tell you that she is leaving us? We shall miss her in Mercy Ward."

"I'm sure you all will," agreed Norah, "and especially Gran Tomkins. . . . Oh, and Sister, may I take my cousin into the ward? Matron said I could show her the Hospital."

"Of course you may. How much have you seen, so far?" she asked Jean.

"Only the children's ward," Jean replied.

"You will find these patients more conscious of their illness than the children," warned Sister. "But remember that they are just the same as any of your own family might have been when they were ill. People are inclined to look upon Hospital patients as a kind of rare curio—something that they could never be themselves—but, of course, they are just as any of us might be. So pretend to be more interested in the ward fittings, and refer occasionally to the human occupants. Then it helps them to feel more like hostesses than a human zoo. Don't you think so, Nurse?"

"Yes, I certainly do," agreed Norah vehemently. "It makes me furious to see visitors eyeing the patients with a morbid curiosity, because they've got ' something-the-matter-with-them.' It's no good shuddering at disease, and anyway it's the patient who has reason to fear, while we more fortunate ones must help them to overcome the fear. But Jean has seen enough to make her want to see more, haven't you, Jean?"

"This way then," said Sister as she moved towards the door.

CHAPTER FOUR

MERCY WARD

GRANNY TOMKINS was entertaining an audience of three. Her hunger for the moment abated, she was in a fine mood to welcome the latest additions to Mercy Ward.

Miss Davis and the elderly Mrs. Bates had only set foot in the hospital that day, and were still feeling a little uncertain about it all. Only Jeannette had been a patient before.

Florence Davis was a young school teacher who had developed a startling habit of jumping into the air whenever one of her pupils dropped a book. From this the pupils had derived much amusement. They dropped book after book.

How could they know that poor Miss Davis cried herself to sleep at night because she felt so tired and cross, and her heart seemed to beat in her throat as if to choke her? They called her the 'cod-fish,' because her eyes looked about to drop from her head. They didn't know that every time Miss Davis heard them it added another weight to the burden of her anxiety.

For, you see, there was something happening

inside Miss Davis that might happen to any of her pupils.

A little gland in front of her throat was producing too much of its own fluid—*thyroxin*—and this thyroxin was running about her body making everything work twice as fast as it should.

So her heart was beating too fast, and her brain was receiving messages and sending them to her muscles at a tremendous speed. This showed when a sudden noise in her ears told her brain to beware, and her brain in turn signalled to her muscles to be "on guard." So even a slight bang made poor Miss Davis jump to attention as though a bomb had been dropped.

All these things made her very tired, just as her pupils would have been tired had she made them do all their lessons twice as fast, and so complete two days' lessons in one day.

Any of her boy pupils could have told her what happens to a boy's eyes when someone is pressing on his wind-pipe. They look as if they might burst.

But no one thought that perhaps their jumping school teacher had something pressing on *her* wind-pipe to make her eyes look so staring and fishy. Yet that was just what was happening.

That same little gland was becoming puffed-up with its own importance. Never before had it felt such a tremendous power. And now . . . lo and behold! . . . even the heart and brain—senior organs of the body—were dancing to the tune it played.

So the horrid little thing grew large and conceited, quite forgetting that it was leaving less and less room for its neighbour, the wind-pipe.

Poor Miss Davis grew more and more breathless, and more and more fish-eyed; till one day, in her misery, she determined to find out what was happening to her body.

It *is* odd how people use their bodies for their own ends during year after year without ever stopping to say, "How are you feeling down there?" Then when some little thing goes on strike—or gets too important for its size they let all the other parts suffer until they, too, start to complain.

Then the owner of this miserable body takes it to a doctor, who shakes his head and says, "Why didn't you come to me before?"

Sometimes the culprit murmurs something about not having the *time*, or being *inconvenient*, which is a poor excuse, because we should all be in a very sorry way if our bodies suddenly said, "I'm off. Working for you isn't convenient just at present."

Fortunately Miss Davis saw a doctor before the gland became quite the master of her body. So now she lay in bed next to Granny Tomkins. It seemed strange to be lying in bed—and not being allowed to put a foot over the side—when yesterday she had cleaned the house from top to bottom, so that her mother need only dust it for a week or so. It had made her *very* tired. And that is why the doctor had said, "It's hospital for you, young lady . . . a nice *long* rest." He knew that you can't be sure that people will rest *completely* at home.

In hospital it is different. The nurses know that you *mustn't* wash yourself even if you *can*, because complete rest is the most important part of the treatment . . . with some medicine to tone down the gland.

So after a while the conceited gland will become disconsolate. He will no longer have the pleasure of hearing the heart leap to his tune, and *he*, also, *will begin to feel tired*. A very good thing for him, too, because otherwise the doctor would have to call in a surgeon and the impudent gland would have to be removed.

It looks, however, as if that isn't going to happen to Miss Davis as she reclines on her pillows listening to Granny Tomkins.

"And the next day they thought I was *gorn*!" said Granny impressively.

She was telling them the history of her illness and had just got past the *relapse*, a part which she enjoyed telling more than any other.

"Yes, they thought it was the end of me," she repeated, shaking her scraggy old head as she turned to Mrs. Bates who had been growing more and more nervous as the history developed.

"It's all right, my dear," Granny's tone was meant to be comforting. "Your case mightn't be the same as mine. They're not *all* as bad. Be it your kidneys, now?"

"Er—no." Mrs. Bates was anxious not to offend an old patient but she had really not been accustomed to talking about the things inside her body. She had always thought they were not very nice things, so it could not be very nice to talk about them.

But Granny's eyes were clear and questioning. She was not to be put off with a vague reply.

"Well . . . er . . . as a matter of fact it's my *stomach* . . . just a little pain, you know." Mrs. Bates stammered in her confusion, and Gran's old face took on a calculating expression.

"That being so," said Gran anxiously. "If it's really yer stummick, that is—and you never can be sure till they've proved it, and that takes the longest time—you'll most likely go on a diet."

"Oh . . . do you think so? Well. Never mind, so long as it's a pleasant one," returned Mrs. Bates brightly.

"Yes," continued Gran, "but *that* being so, what'll you do with all the food your visitors bring you? You can't *eat* it, y'know."

"Can't I? Oh dear . . . I hadn't thought . . . perhaps they won't bring any," suggested Mrs. Bates.

"Oh yes, they will," Gran insisted. "Relations

you didn't 'ardly know you 'ad 'll turn up . . . and they'll all bring *something* to eat, because you can't go to a 'orspital empty-'anded, and flowers is expensive these days. Good thing, too, I says; grub is better. But now, if you *do* ever have difficulty about having too much that you can't eat . . . not being allowed, you know . . . I'll 'elp you out. I 'elped Mrs. Atkins out with a few chocolate éclairs, to save the cream going sour in them, being as the weather was 'ot, and Mrs. Atkins rather averse to chocolate éclairs at the time."

"Oooh . . . *chocolate éclairs!*" Jeanette's voice was rapturous. "I can't ever have them though."

"Why not, ducks?"

"*Sugar* . . . I'm in here 'cos I've got too much sugar in my blood."

Granny looked interested. "There now, have you, dearie? And how old are you?"

"Fourteen."

"Only fourteen and she knows all about it. There now; there's a case." Gran was frankly admiring.

"So I should, by now," returned Jeannette perkily. "I've had it for five years. It's nothing much. I've been in here before; in the children's ward. St. Anne's that is. 'Slovely; all glass."

"Don't you *never* get better though, dearie?" inquired Gran anxiously.

"I'm nearly always all right except if I eat the

wrong food . . . or forget to have my injection . . . but I never do now, so I'm fine."

"What you in here for now, then?" insisted Gran.

"Because my tests have proved me a bit too sugary lately, so I've come in to have my diet overlooked. Maybe they'll say I must eat more, and give me more insulin too."

"What's *insulin*?" Gran felt it wasn't right, this kid knowing so much more than an old stager like herself. But the kid seemed to be an old stager too, so that made it easier.

Jeannette thought for a moment before answering. "Well," she began. "I've got too much sugar in my blood because I haven't got enough insulin in my pancreas—that's the place where the insulin is stored—so I just have to put the insulin in with a needle. It doesn't hurt if you do it quickly. I've done it for years."

Miss Davis shot forward in her bed. "*You've given yourself the injections?*"

"You bet. I wouldn't have any old person jabbing needles into *my* arm. It's different the nurses and doctors, of course, but before I went home the first time, they taught me how to prick myself. All the girls at school wanted to do it, too; but *they* can't; they're not diabetics."

"But," Miss Davis still leaned forward in her bed looking across Mrs. Bates to Jeannette, "but you were only *nine* five years ago!"

"That's right; never too young to learn," sang Jeannette cheerfully.

"Well, I'm blowed!" Even Grannie had forgotten to go on with the history of her interesting recovery from the relapse. "If you aren't a plucky young kid. Now . . . tell us more about this 'ere *insulin*, so long as you're not fibbing. Now don't you *fib*, or I'll tell the doctor on you!"

"He'll tell you exactly the same as I do, if you ask him," returned Jeannette, unabashed, and she settled down to explain.

"It all starts with your food, because *it* contains sugar."

"What if it don't?" interrupted Mrs. Bates. "What if you don't like sweet things and don't never have sugar in your tea?"

"You'd still have it." Jeannette dismissed the interruption airily. "Perhaps you don't know that there is sugar in all the carbohydrates."

"The *what*?"

"*Carbohydrates*. Starches—bread, potatoes, cereals bananas, milk . . . and lots more. So that you always get sugar with your food."

"*Well*, now!"

"Then," insisted Jeannette, because she was enjoying it, "this sugar should be properly distributed by the insulin from your pancreas . . . or your needle . . . the sugar doesn't mind which."

"Sounds too easy for a proper illness," burst in Gran doubtfully.

"Oh no, it isn't," flashed Jean. "There's lots more to it. Once you've had your insulin, you must eat the amount of food it is meant to work on. Too much insulin with no work to do is as bad as not enough."

"Then what?" challenged Gran.

"You go to sleep."

"Well, if that ain't nice and comfy. Call that a disease!" Gran was scornful. "Sounds more like a health cure."

"*But*," added Jeannette with triumph, "*what if you don't wake up again?*"

Granny Tomkins' jaw dropped in consternation. A *proper* illness and no mistake!

"Coo," said she. "Then you'd be *gorn*."

"*No*," said the mischievous child. "Wrong again. Doctor just pours sugar into you and you wake up."

Gran was shaking her head in bewilderment.

"Quite like ring-a-ring-a-roses," said Mrs. Bates breezily. "You never know who'll fall down first."

Miss Davis said nothing at all. During the last months of anxiety she had almost grown to hate the children who taunted her. Now here was one who had answered the challenge of ill-health. Those other children hadn't taunted *her*. They had envied her instead. That was because Jeannette had refused to be overpowered by fear of the unknown. She had gone out to meet and understand it . . . to discipline it to her will.

Then Miss Davis remembered some of the stories she loved most in the history that she taught her pupils.

Stories of brave men and women who had lived for the benefit of mankind. Many of them had broken bodies . . . but their spirit was alive and lived long after them.

Robert Louis Stevenson who had travelled through the Cevennes with a donkey because of the disease which had affected his lungs. For many years after he contributed to the world of literature. His stories are as popular to-day as they ever were. She had told her pupils of his courage when they were reading his *Travels with a Donkey*.

But there was no need to delve into the past for people who, because of their afflictions, had found a special work to do.

Thousands of people every week were entertained by the humorous drawings of Fougasse, the man who only discovered that he could draw when he was forced by an accident to lie on his back for a long time. Only his hands had been free to amuse him. Now they amused the world.

Then there was the founder of St. Dunstan's, the great institution for the blind. Sir Arthur Pearson had to be blinded himself before he realised what a tremendous need there was for such a place as St.

Dunstan's. A place where a man's sight might be saved if it were possible, and if not, where his hands could be taught to do without the guidance of his eyes.

So stands St. Dunstan's, an institution known and loved by the blind all the world over. A home, hospital and school whence blinded men come back into the world as a useful part of it. Through one brave, blind man, the pride of all the blind remains inviolate.

Dame Agnes Hunt, a cripple herself, founded the first open-air hospital for cripples. She started a new fashion in the treatment of bone diseases. Fresh air and sunshine came into the lives of her patients . . . so they thrived, and many were no longer crippled. That was all because *she* knew what it meant to be deformed, and knowing, set herself against deformity . . . and won.

Would Viscount Snowden ever have become the Chancellor of the Exchequer had he not educated himself with books, during a long and crippling illness?

And the man whose name was once a household word, Franklin D. Roosevelt. The whole world hung in breathless suspense for his decision. War . . . or subjection. He chose war because he would not subject himself to a social deformity any more than he had subjected himself to his physical deformity.

Franklin D. Roosevelt was an athlete with an athlete's joy of physical well-being, before an attack of poliomyelitis robbed him of his life of sport. There remained to him the life of his mind; a great mind. So he became the President of the United States of America.

There has always been such courage; there always will be. The people who look out at life and love it, will not easily be dwarfed by self-pity.

Florence Davis was beginning to find comfort in a new strength; a strength which would allow her to face her affliction . . . and defy it. That was what she was doing now, by lying quietly in bed.

She relaxed farther into her pillows and stretched her toes luxuriously at the bottom of the bed.

Yes, she would defy that gland. Defy it by resting . . . and *resting* . . . and taking all the medicine she was given. Her gland wanted her to rush about all over the place, and jump, and get irritable. But she'd *show* it. She just *wouldn't*.

But all the same she *did* jump when Granny Tomkins suddenly jerked up in bed and, collecting sundry newspapers, bags, and boxes, stuffed them into bed with her.

" 'Ere's *Sister*," said Gran, as she straightened her top-sheet and took out her knitting like the industrious little woman she liked to appear. " *With visitors, too*," she added, cocking a bright old eye at the door. Then down went the knitting.

"*Nurse Brown!*" cried Granny joyfully.

"Yes," said Sister. "I've brought her back to see you." And she explained to Jean, "Your cousin was working for me in this ward until a fortnight ago, and her patients still miss her. Strange, isn't it?" she laughed.

Dear Gran was almost lost for words as Norah walked up to her bed and stood laughing down at her.

"And how's Grandma Tomkins. Still as hungry as ever?" inquired Norah.

"I'm well, thank you, dearie. How's yourself?" As Granny returned the greeting, one hand strayed beneath the bedclothes, smoothing out a lump.

"Dear Grandma, what big *bumps* you've got!" teased Norah as she moved on after Sister and Jean.

Sister was showing Jean the oxygen cylinder which stood by the side of an empty bed.

"This bed is always ready for an acute case," explained Sister. "We have a casualty ward to which emergency patients usually go, but if the case is already diagnosed before admission—perhaps by the patient's private doctor—and is to be a long time recovering, we usually take her straight in here. Long cases are not kept in Casualty. They are moved to whichever ward they are most suited for, so if they are medical and come straight here, it saves their being moved a few days later."

"But the bed isn't made, is it?" asked Jean. "It looks a funny shape beneath the counterpane."

"Oh, yes it is," answered Sister, as she swept back the white counterpane which lay loosely over the bed.

Jean stared in wonderment.

"It hasn't got any sheets on it," she cried.

"Yes it has, but they are covered by these old blankets. When an emergency patient comes in she is often very cold and tired and must have blankets next to her for a while to make her warm again. Then when she is warm and rested and fit for it, we gently wash her between these blankets. It doesn't matter if the blankets get a tiny bit damp because we take them away afterwards and leave her fresh and clean between the sheets."

"However can you wash any one if they are covered by a blanket?"

"Well, we very carefully expose a small part of the body at a time—first an arm, and then a leg, and so on—so that the patient never feels cold as most of her body is warm beneath the blankets," explained Sister.

"I see. But why can't you tuck the bed up properly?" pressed Jean.

"Now, think what happens when you get into bed. You pull down the top and climb up, then you push your legs down between the bedclothes that are tucked in. That takes quite a lot of movement but the patient who comes in here in a great hurry is often very ill and can't move much. We lift her into bed. So, don't you see, it is much easier to have the bedclothes folded to one side *all the way down the bed*, so that she can either roll from the trolley or be lifted? Then we just roll the clothes over her to the other side of the bed and tuck them in."

"Yes, that makes it easier," agreed Jean.

"But do you notice anything strange about the bed itself?" asked Sister.

"It *does* seem to have a lot of bars and things underneath it," said Jean, bending down to see more of them.

"Here's why," answered Sister, and she started to wind a handle at the back of the bed. Immediately the head of the bed began to rise, until the whole bed looked like a gigantic armchair.

"Whatever does it do that for?" cried Jean.

"If the patient is suffering from pneumonia or a bad heart, she will find breathing very difficult. In that case a sitting position will help her to get her breath. So then we just wind up the bed so that it supports her in an upright position.

"Such patients often need some oxygen to help their breathing. So we keep a cylinder close by and turn on this handle to make the oxygen pour out through the funnel. The patient can quite easily hold the funnel and take lovely, deep breaths of *very* fresh air.

"We don't leave the bed up like this though," said Sister, as she wound it down again. "It is more usual for an emergency admission to be cold and shocked, in which case it is better that they should be flat for a while. We can even raise the *foot* of the bed on these big blocks."

She pointed to two wooden blocks on the floor beneath the bed.

"How does that help them?" inquired Jean.

"Well, you know that when anyone has a fright they often turn pale. Usually only for a moment. That is because the blood supply to the head fails. If the shock is bad this may last longer than for just a moment. Then to raise the foot of the bed helps to send the blood back into the heart and brain."

Jean turned to Norah.

"No wonder that you say you *like* the hard work in a hospital. It *must* be thrilling; seeing so many people and helping them in so many different ways."

"*It is*," declared Norah, as they stood for a moment in the doorway, looking down the long ward.

Twelve evenly spaced beds stood round against the cool green walls. Between each a little scrubbed locker held a jug of water, a glass, and some books. In each bed a figure rested against soft pillows, under a smooth white counterpane.

The three next to Grannie were deep in conversation. Other heads were turned together in eager consultation, whilst some tired eyes turned for refreshment to the flowers on the long centre table.

"They *are* pretty," said Jean, noting the clever arrangement of lilac and rhododendron blooms.

"Visitors are very generous, aren't they, Nurse?" said Sister, turning to Norah.

"Yes, indeed. Sometimes it is even difficult to know where to put all the flowers. Every window sill and ledge has to be used for floral decoration, as I well know," answered Norah ruefully. "The *hours* I've spent arranging flowers!"

"And liking it, too," put in Sister.

"Perhaps," admitted Norah grudgingly, and then, the grudge gone from her voice: "Anything to make them happy."

"Yes, indeed." Sister explained to Jean. "Just for a time these women cease to be a part of a household or an office. While they are with us they are *each* important; each *different* from the other, and each with a special story of her own.

"The story of how she came to be ill, what she will do to get better, and how she will live afterwards.

"The first part of her story was told before she came here. We dictate the second and *suggest* the third.

"That is the privilege of our work, that we are

in a position to help, not only with their illness, but in the new life that will follow it.

"And that, I think, is what your cousin means when she says she *likes* the hard work of a hospital nurse."

Norah nodded.

CHAPTER FIVE

THE THEATRE

"WE'LL GO to the theatre next," announced Norah, after they had said good-bye to Sister at the door of Mercy Ward. "They've been busy here this afternoon, so you'll see signs of some operating."

She led the way past the main entrance to three more white doors at the far end of the Hospital. The middle door said "Anæsthetic Room" and Norah cautiously opened it and peeped inside.

"It's all right," she said. "They're finished," and she opened the door wide for Jean to follow her through.

Jean gasped on the threshold.

"That smell again . . . and stronger than ever!" she cried involuntarily.

"Yes, this is where it all comes from. Wait here for a moment while I ask if the coast is clear." Norah disappeared through a side door towards the sound of clattering enamel and upraised voices.

Jean stared around. She was standing in a small square room. Rather like the duty-room in Mercy Ward, she thought, only even more smelling and glittering . . . and *very* light.

The window took up most of the far wall and beneath it stood a table laid with bottles and glittering instruments. A wash-basin and a white painted wardrobe filled in the two far corners, while a desk at one end faced an assortment of cylinders at the other. The centre of the stone floor was quite bare.

Jean was just taking a few tentative steps towards the cylinders to investigate their elaborate fittings when Norah hailed her from a side door.

"You can come in," she said. "They're all in the middle of clearing up from this afternoon's operations, but Sister's off-duty and Nurse says we may look about. You won't have to touch anything without asking, though, in case it's meant to be sterile. Come on."

"Aren't you going to show this to me first?" Jean hesitated, with one eye still on the cylinders.

"All right, if you're so keen," laughed Norah.

"Well, I don't want to miss anything, and these look important enough to be explained." Jean moved more confidently towards a group of cylinders which stood together in a white enamel stand, entangled with an array of rubber tubing and bright silver clips and screws.

"A complicated looking affair," she remarked.

"That's just an anæsthetic stand. Those cylinders contain gas and oxygen. The gas is nitrous oxide, of course, *not* the same as you have in your gas-oven at home."

"Yes, but how does it work?" insisted Jean.

Smiling, Norah picked up a double trail of rubber tubing. "These are fastened to a rubber mask. When that is placed over the patient's face and the cylinder keys turned, the anæsthetic flows down the tubing into the mask and is inhaled by the patient. You see, one tube is attached to the oxygen and the other to the gas. Together they form a very safe anæsthetic."

She stooped to a lower shelf underneath the table and brought out a heavy rubber mask with straps.

Jean shuddered. "It must be frightening to have one's face covered with that. Doesn't the patient feel that she is smothering?"

"Not often these days," said Norah, consolingly. "Very few patients are awake when they come in here. They have already had a sleeping-drug injected while still in the ward. Sometimes they have what is known as ' twilight sleep,' which is just two drugs combining to produce a happy state of semi-consciousness in which the patient loses all fear. Other patients have a stronger drug injected and are completely unconscious when they arrive here. It all depends on their previous condition, but in either case, they don't mind the mask being put over their face."

"What was it that Sister said in the children's ward about Tommy Tucker *blowing up a balloon*?"

"Oh, she meant this." Norah pointed to a col-

lapsed rubber bag which fitted on to the mask.
"When the anæsthetic is flowing, the extent of the
flow is registered on the metres attached to the
cylinders. As the patient breathes in the anæsthetic
the balloon moves in and out showing the extent
of his breathing.

" If the breathing becomes too shallow it shows in
the size and shape of the balloon, and the anæsthetist
turns off a little gas and puts more pressure on the
oxygen. The anæsthetic can be made to suit each
patient.

"We often explain to children about the balloon
because it interests them and they forget to be
frightened."

"Aren't they asleep when they come in here,
then?" inquired Jean, anxiously.

"No, not often. We can't give them very strong
injections so at the most they are only sleepy."
Norah laughed. "A lot of them are too excited
even for that. I once saw a little boy who was
going to have his tonsils out push his own trolley
through the theatre door.

"Of course, all the patients are wheeled in here
on a trolley. They remain on it to have their
anæsthetic and then when the theatre doors are
opened in goes the whole procession. The patient
on the trolley, the anæsthetist with his own trolley
attached to the patient by these tubes, and the
ward-nurse—or sister—in charge of the case. The

surgeon and theatre nurses are waiting ready to receive it. . . . But come and see the nurses; they're busy at the moment."

Norah led her towards the sound of clattering enamel, running water, and young voices. Never before had Jean looked upon a scene of such activity At first it was difficult to pick out the nurses from the piles of white linen that stood about.

"This is the sterilising-room," said Norah, indicating the steamy enclosure. And then Jean noticed the great silver tanks that she had seen before in the duty-room of Mercy Ward, only here they were much bigger and there were more of them.

Through the steam that poured from its open lid, a nurse was poking into the depths of one of them with a long pair of forceps, while water gushed from the relief pipe down into the drain below.

"Crikey!" said the nurse, ungrudgingly, as she hauled forth a tiny bowl on the end of the forceps only to lose it again with a splash and a clatter. The pile of bowls and dishes on the floor beside her, bore witness to her task. She was emptying and cleaning the sterilisers.

"All those bowls have to be cleaned and stacked inside the clean steriliser ready to be boiled up again in the morning," explained Norah. "Unless, of course, there's an emergency case to-night. But then they usually boil up a few of them in one of the smaller sterilisers."

"Twenty-three, twenty-four, twenty-five . . . ah, here it is, twenty-*six*!" sang a voice from the other side of the room. "Thank goodness that's the lot . . . coming Smithy!" and with an awful clatter a pile of glittering instruments were poured into a bowl of soapy water presided over by Smithy. She lovingly hauled each one forth to dry and polish it carefully.

"Now we've only got the cutting instruments left . . . haven't we?" she inquired solicitously.

"Yes, and they're clean, they just need polishing . . . oh, hallo! . . . here she is. Hope she doesn't mind the mess," said the singing voice as its owner spotted Norah with Jean.

"Not at all," answered Norah cheerfully. "It'll give her the local colour. Jean, this is Nurse Jackson D'you remember my speaking of Hilda Jackson who was at college with me? It's the very same girl. *She* cribbed the idea from me!"

Norah moved on to avoid a slap from a very wet towel, and nearly fell over a pile of linen.

"Sluicing," she explained, as she recovered her balance.

"I beg your pardon?" queried Jean.

"All these towels have been used on the operating-table. Some of them are blood-stained and have to be sluiced before they are sent to the laundry. It comes out in no time in cold water, so long as you don't give it time to dry first . . . doesn't it, Nurse?"

She turned to a young probationer who stood over a sink of water. She was eyeing a pile of wet clean towels with pride.

"Have you got to wash all these?" asked Jean faintly, as she pointed to the huge pile that Norah had nearly fallen over.

"Oh no; we don't wash any of them. They go to the laundry. But first we look through them for any stains and put those to soak in cold water. Then, when they are wrung out, they go to the laundry with the others," the little probationer explained obligingly.

"Is that what you meant by *sluicing* them?" asked Jean of Norah.

"That's right. We have a specially strong hose to turn on them so that they almost do themselves." Norah unhooked a heavy rubber hose from the wall above the sink and turned on a small tap. Immediately a strong jet of water spurted into the sink below. As Norah turned a clip on the hose, the jet became a spray.

"Labour-saving," she remarked briefly, and led Jean towards a small door in the back of the room.

"The theatre kitchen," she announced, and Jean peered into a little cubby-hole which held a miniature scrubbed dresser, and a tap and gas-ring. Against the scrubbed woodwork hung a plentiful array of brightly flowered cups.

"Sometimes there isn't time to break-off at the

proper time for tea in the dining-room," Norah explained. "So they have it here when the operating is over. They prefer to, anyway."

"You bet we do." Nurse Jackson had followed them in. "We're going to have some now as a matter of fact, although having finished early we *could* get over to the dining-room. However, the worst part of the mess is cleared up now, so we might as well have a breather. *We* don't have time for any after-lunch cups of tea, as these ward folk do." She eyed Norah defensively. "What about it? Have some?"

"We might as well, now that we're here, if Jean can drink two lots. I've arranged for tea in my room after I've shown her the Hospital." Norah promptly made herself comfortable on the edge of the little bread-bin and pulled a small stool forward for Jean.

Jackson perched on the edge of the dresser from which point of vantage she filled the kettle under the tap and placed it on the gas-ring. From over her head she hauled down a tin box and two china plates. The tea was laid. Hearing the sound of china, the nurses of the steriliser, instruments, and sink took their places in the doorway.

"The nurses Bates, Hart and Fuller," introduced Norah airily. "We're staying for our first tea," she added.

"Is your cousin as bad as you?" inquired Nurse Hart.

"If you're referring to my tea-drinking habit, *no*, I shouldn't think it's possible," answered Norah modestly, "but she has *other* vices."

"And tea isn't one of them, but it *will* be if she comes near a hospital too often. I've been smitten now. I only drank it once a day at home, but here . . . it's comforting."

"How much have you seen of the Hospital?" Nurse Bates asked Jean.

"Two wards and their side-regions, and . . . here, or at least, *some* of here."

"*Brownie!* . . . Haven't you taken her into the theatre?" Bates turned to Norah.

"Give me a chance. She spent ages inquiring after anæsthetics and now you've lured us into here. But I will show them to her after I've swallowed this." And she raised the cup to her lips again.

"It's all right, there's no hurry," Jean demurred. "Anyhow I can't see an operation now . . . it's too late, but I *would* like to . . . only . . . might I faint?"

"Of course not, why on earth should you?" Bates's voice was strongly derisive.

"I just thought people *did* when they first saw one. Didn't you feel anything at all?"

"Excitement, of course, but nothing more deadly."

"O-oh . . . I shan't ever forget the first time I walked in the theatre!" Poor little Fuller, the probationer of the sluicing, shuddered.

"Why, was it something messy?" asked Norah with some surprise.

All the theatre-nurses were laughing.

"*She* made the mess," said Smithy. "Go on, tell her about it."

"It was before I came to work in the theatre," started little Fuller. "I was on the men's surgical ward and we had a long list of ops. that day. Sister was taking the cases into the theatre, but as fast as one came out, the surgeon would start on the one in the next theatre. So I had to bring the cases to the theatre, hand them over to Sister, and then escort the finished cases back to the ward.

"I was feeling awfully important and enjoying it until nearly the end of the afternoon, when Sister didn't appear from the theatre to take over the case I had brought. She seemed an unusually long time fixing up the last case and the next one had already been anæsthetised and taken into the second theatre.

"Imagine my horror when the theatre sister sent a message out to inquire *who* was the ward-nurse in charge of the case and would she come in *at once*.

"I'd never so much as put a foot over the theatre threshold before and I knew that there were all sorts of pitfalls, but one of the stretcher-bearers tied me into a gown and mask and prompted me to cover my shoes with galoshes.

"I staggered through the door with the patient's

chart, bandage, and china vomit bowl to find the group of white-clad figures waiting expectantly round the theatre table.

"The next moment that china bowl lay shattered on the floor and I was miserably crouching over the pieces which I could hardly see through the tears of my mortification. It was awful!

"Then Sister came. She took in the situation at a glance and went straight up to the patient and removed the guard. After that she let me stay in the theatre with her, so that I should know what to do another time."

Fuller shook her head and gasped with the memory of the occasion, as her audience laughed.

"What do you mean by the *guard* . . . you said it had to be removed?" asked Jean.

"*Sterile guard*," they chorused, and Norah explained. "The area for operation has to be thoroughly cleaned . . . shaved if necessary . . . and painted with an antiseptic such as iodine or surgical spirit. Then there will be no harmful organisms near the new wound. All this is done in the ward to save time in the theatre. But it wouldn't be any good doing it if the patient's theatre-gown—which, of course, is clean but not sterile—was allowed to touch it. So a sterile *guard* —just a piece of lint or a towel—is placed over the prepared area and lightly bound on with cotton bandages which can be cut as soon as the patient is anæsthetised. Then just before the surgeon operates, the guard is carefully lifted away and the area surrounded by sterile mackintoshes and towels, over which the surgeon may work without contaminating himself. He, and his assistants too, are dressed in sterile linen from head to foot. There is no chance of infection that way."

"What a palaver!" gasped Jean.

"You bet it is," agreed Smithy. "But it's all absolutely necessary. Why, almost every movement is prearranged so that a newcomer entering into the ritual feels much as she would if she found herself on a stage not knowing a word of her part. In her nervousness she may easily stumble against something she shouldn't touch, and get shouted at; not because any one disapproves of her, but because they try to stop her before she does it. Then the poor unfortunate has the agony of watching a complete tray of instruments having to be replaced by fresh ones, or seeing a surgeon tear off his gown and start to scrub up all over again.

"Of course, when you understand the very necessary theatre formality it doesn't affect you in the least; you don't even notice it."

"At first, the strangest thing to me," interrupted Fuller, "was when the operation was under way, and the surgeon was chatting about everything under the sun and appeared not to be thinking of the operation at all.

"I was just beginning to think 'callous brute!' when he stopped in the middle of his chatty conversation and said, 'How old is she? Any children? We must go carefully; she may want a family.' And then I realised that he hadn't forgotten that he was working on a human-being with her own plans for living. She was more than just a case. I was amazed!"

"So would many people be amazed," agreed Norah. "Some of them have an idea that surgeons just like cutting things out because it is their job. But I've always felt that when they *have* to remove something, they do it with a certain amount of regret."

She rose with a clatter from the bread bin.

"Well, so long, girls . . . and thanks for the tea. It'll keep us going for the rest of the tour."

"Where else are you going?" asked Smith as she saw them to the door.

"Out-patients, X-ray, the P.T.S. and the Home," answered Norah. "But I'll just show her the theatre on the way out."

"Yes, do. I won't come with you because we've not finished clearing-up yet, and there's a blood donor coming at six o'clock."

"Right, we'll leave you to it. Come on, Jean. Good-bye!"

"What's a blood donor?" asked Jean as they passed through the sterilising room on their way out.

"A person who volunteers to give blood whenever any is needed for a transfusion. They have plenty to spare of their own, and after undergoing a test to see if they are suitable, they are entered on a list. Then when we need any of their group of blood—there are four groups, you see—we get into touch with them and they come up here and give it.

"The process is quite simple. If we take a whole pint, they sometimes feel a bit shivery afterwards, but a cup of strong coffee or tea soon puts that right. And, of course, we only take as much as they can well afford to lose."

"I suppose somebody must have offered their blood for the baby we saw in St. Anne's ward?" remarked Jean thoughtfully.

"Oh yes, they had . . . but probably one of the parents in that case. They often offer it for their small children. But they are not official blood donors, and if they are not suitable we have to refuse such an offer. The official donors are ready to give their blood for anybody at all and often don't know to whom it is given. Rather funny, when you come to think of it. They may sit opposite somebody in a train and never know that they have saved that person's life."

Jean was thoughtful as Norah led her past huge glass cupboards of glittering instruments and through another large white door.

The north wall of the square theatre was entirely

glass, so that the light was white and clear. In addition a huge lamp hung from the ceiling.

"Shadowless," Norah explained, "and it can be moved on this hinge."

Jean had never seen such an enormous lamp. It was twice as big as her bicycle wheel, and when Norah touched a switch in the wall, it shed a clear, *clear* light. Hardly *bright*, thought Jean, because it was in no way glaring.

The floors and walls were of stone and tiles respectively, as they were in all the other rooms of the unit. "That's because they can all be washed so easily," explained Norah.

Under the lamp stood the operating table, a quiet and powerful monument to the amazing history of surgery.

Norah pressed a pedal underneath it, and the whole thing lifted to a higher level. Another pedal lowered it. Another tilted it.

"So, you see, we can arrange the patient in any position we require," she announced.

There was very little furniture in the room. Just a row of sinks, and two large marble slabs. One held tall enamel jugs and silver drums. "We keep the sterile lotions and dressings in those," explained Norah.

Near the window stood two tall stands, such as Jean had seen holding the flask of blood for the baby in St. Anne's ward.

"Irrigating stands," Norah explained. "If we want to wash out a wound, the fluid has to be hanging at a higher level to give pressure to the flow. Then we can regulate it with clips and screws."

As Jean's eyes travelled up in wonderment, she saw a gallery running round the top of the room.

"Is that for the audience?"

"Yes, the students, and any nurses who are off duty and wish to come out of interest. The other theatre is almost the same; a little smaller perhaps," she said as she finally led the way to the door. "I'll show it to you as we go out. It's the other side of the anæsthetic room."

Jean peeped in at another display of shining cleanliness.

"And not a single germ," she whispered in triumphant awe, as the door thumped heavily, and echoed around them.

"Not if we can help it," laughed Norah.

CHAPTER SIX

O.P.D.

"THAT spot of tea has just given me an appetite for our proper one," said Norah, as they left the theatre. "So I think we'll go over and have it now; it's getting latish. We can go out the back way so that I can show you the Out-Patient Department on the way out."

She captured the lift. "All the way down to the basement this time," she announced.

Their feet echoed on the old scrubbed boards of the rambling department which had been built on to the basement of the Hospital, where the ground sloped away down hill. As they passed into a square hall full of long wooden forms, there came the sound of smothered laughter from one of the rooms which led off it, followed by the sound of moving furniture and the brisk footsteps of a nurse who appeared in the doorway holding a duster and tin of polish as though they were weapons of defence.

Immediately she saw Norah with Jean, the look of businesslike abstraction vanished from her face, and she was laughing.

"Oh it's *you*," she gasped. Her next words were

flung over her shoulder to the room she had just left. "It's all right . . . only Brownie . . . you can carry on."

And "Out-patients" echoed with their mirth.

Norah was laughing, too. "What *are* you up to? No good, I'll be bound . . .! What on earth!"

For now the very walls seemed to shake as a fresh peal of abandoned laughter hurtled round the empty hall.

At that moment another figure appeared in the doorway, bent almost double. Clutching the doorpost for support, it swayed from side to side in a delightful agony of mirth. Twice . . . three times, it spluttered, and at last formed the words. "It's Hunt . . . come and see!"

So they all moved towards the room, the first nurse explaining: "We were trying on some mudpacks."

And then they saw.

Standing in a far door of the room they had entered was an apparition. From the feet up to the neck it was a nurse. After that there was a greeny grey pool, from which two eyes looked despairingly out, and in the middle—a mouth laughed! The result was, at once, both comic and grotesque.

Despair was reflected in the droop of "its" hands— also besmeared with the mud mixture—and in the blobs of mud which trailed into the room "it" had evidently just left.

Nobody attempted to offer an explanation. The first nurse was just a crumpled heap behind Jean, who stared first at the apparition and then at the effect "it" had produced on "its" audience. Another nurse had simply lowered her head on to her folded arms, and, using the table as her support, she silently shook from head to foot. Norah and Jean were rapidly sinking to the same level of helplessness.

At last Nurse No. 1, whose name turned out to be Davis, took a deep and painful breath and said with a sob in her voice: "You see, we heard your footsteps and thought it was Dainty Doris . . . so poor old Hunt . . ." she nodded towards the apparition ". . . took fright and . . ."

". . . *tried to pull it off!*" The head rose from the table. "You should have *seen* her, Brownie . . . uttering squeaks of dismay and . . . *pulling* it from her face like chewing gum. Then she . . . she put her head under the table to hide it . . . *and left the rest of her sticking out* . . . with lumps of mud all round. I've *never* seen anything so funny!" And down went the head again as its owner gave herself up to another paroxysm.

"So *this* is how you spend your time when you should be working!" Norah's tone was more severe than her expression.

"Go it, Brownie! I seem to remember a certain occasion . . ." but Norah stopped her with the tin of polish poised.

Jean was curious about the mud mixture and sidled towards the apparition who, having got her face to some soap and water, was rapidly regaining human form. When eventually she peeped over the towel, with which she vigorously dried herself, Jean was looking at a glowing pink and white complexion and into two warm brown eyes. Hunt returned her gaze. "You must be Brownie's cousin," she said.

"Yes, I am," and then Jean added, because she simply *had* to know. "What *was* it on your face?"

Nurse Hunt laughed, this time only an easy chuckle.

"We call them facial cocktails. Just oatmeal, almond oil, and a little peroxide. It should have the white of two eggs and some lemon juice in it, but it's kind of expensive. The main thing is *not* to laugh when you've got it on . . . but, of course, we always do, which spoils the good effect."

"What does it do though?" insisted Jean curiously.

"As it dries on your face it should tighten, and that is supposed to make the facial muscles tighten too . . . so they say. Of course, if you laugh it cracks the mask. Mine hasn't had any effect at all to-day. I'd just got it on"—she laughed at the recollection—"when we heard your footsteps. S-so I tried to pull it off in a hurry. But it has to be *washed* off. I thought it was our assistant Matron coming, so I had to hide my head somewhere. Silly, wasn't it . . . Here's Dolly; she's come to see what it was all about."

"I *never* 'eard such a row. Wot *was* you up to?" the figure in the doorway beamed at them all as though their noise had endeared them even more to her. Jean recognised her uniform as that of a Hospital cleaner. Over her large white apron hung a second one of sacking and in her hand she clutched a floorcloth. "Just couldn't wait another second to 'ear wot it all was. I left me floor and come along to see for myself. You *are* a lot and no mistake. The 'ole 'orspital fair rockin' with the noise of *yer* . . . oh, I *see* . . .!" Her eyes caught sight of the splashes of oatmeal on the floor. "Them *packs* again!" she said darkly.

"It was me, Dolly." Hunt's laughing face belied her humble tone. "But don't you worry, I'll clear it up."

"You'll do no such thing. Sloppin' round spoilin' yer hands wot needs to look nice fer them dressin's. Floors is my province . . . and nurses is my blight." With which sombre philosophy she departed to fetch a pail of water.

"Dear old Dolly," said Norah.

"She's a marvel," agreed Hunt. "But you wait till she comes back to give me a lecture on mudpacks." Hunt threw herself into an attitude resembling Dolly. "Did you put it on *even*?" she mimicked. "Now, Nurse 'Unt, it ain't no good puttin' them packs on and then pullin' them off again . . . an' laughin' . . . that's wot you do, laugh . . . and spoil the lot." Nurse Hunt pretended to slosh water over the floor, and then, wringing out an imaginary floor-cloth, she continued naughtily: "When my young Bette does 'er face she sits quiet and proper, not talkin', nor laughin', nor nothin' . . . just sittin' . . ." She broke off as Dolly reappeared with a bucket.

"Not much chance of 'sittin' proper' here," murmured Norah as she led Jean out of the room with Davis following behind.

"Now, Nurse 'Unt, did you go *laughin'* again . . ." Dolly's voice sailed after them.

"She was the light of our existence when I was working down here," said Norah, referring to Dolly. "She'd entertain us for hours with stories of her Bette, and her Bette's young men and what Pa threatens to do to the young man that brings her home a minute after 10 p.m.!"

They were passing through the hall with its rows of wooden benches, which, Norah explained to Jean, were for the out-patients to sit upon whilst waiting for the doctor to see them.

Nurse Davis had suddenly become embarrassed, wondering if Jean thought that the Out-patient staff were not in the habit of working. "We have only had a morning clinic to-day," she explained.

"So, of course, the department is closed and we are finished early. . . ."

"And are spending the rest of the day in lawful cleaning," interrupted Norah, meaningly.

"We worked like Trojans until nearly four o'clock," demurred Davis. "Then Hunt was finished first so . . ."

"But what do you have to work at if there are no clinics," broke in Jean.

"Cleaning . . . always cleaning," sang Norah.

So Davis explained. "By the end of the day the clinics are looking a bit untidy and most of the instruments have been used, so we tidy up and prepare fresh instruments for the next day. If you come in here I'll show you."

They went into another room on the other side of the main hall. It contained simply a table, half a dozen chairs and a pair of scales.

"Everything is cleaned and put away for to-morrow," said Davis, opening a drawer in the table. It held notepaper, various official-looking forms, blotting-paper, pens and paper-clips. Another drawer seemed at first to contain only a clean white towel, but between its folds were hidden some instruments which Jean had seen used before. A flat tongue-depresser which Doctor Miles always used for looking into her throat when it was sore, and the little round mirror on a long handle which he used when the soreness was *very* far down. A torch and another heavy instrument which Norah affectionately termed a "patella hammer." "For testing your jerks," she said, and before Jean could discover what that meant, she was whisked into a tiny room beyond. This contained a couch and a chair. A pillow and two folded blankets lay on the chair.

"This is where the patient is examined," announced Nurse Davis.

"Do they see the doctor in the other room first?"

"Yes, but first of all, before the clinic actually starts, we weigh every patient; this is a medical clinic, you see. If it was a surgical one we would collect any X-rays they may have had taken, so that when the surgeon starts to interview the patient, he has all his collected evidence before him.

"Every patient has collected her notes from the clerk at the desk in the main hall; did you notice it?"

"Yes," answered Jean, "isn't it the long desk running along the front of the waiting hall?"

"That's right, and behind it are all the files of every patient who has attended this hospital ever since it was founded in 1916.

"So, first the patient collects her notes—as we call them—which contain the history and treatment of her disease. Each time she visits us the date is stamped in the column and by it we write her weight. Then the doctor adds any remarks about her progress or his change of treatment.

"So, you see, we have to be very accurate about the weight because whether a person is gaining or losing is a vital point in most diseases. Sometimes it is good for them to lose, of course."

"Don't you ever take X-rays for medical cases?"

"Oh yes, quite often, but not so often as for surgical ones who are almost invariably X-rayed at some time or another."

"Do you use this room for surgical clinics, too?"

"No, we use the one on the other side because it has a little theatre and sterilising room adjoining it. Sometimes, you see, there are minor operations to be performed during or after the surgical clinics. If someone comes up with a cyst (a small growth), or a deep cut, or a splinter in their hand, they usually can have it attended to right away. Perhaps you'd like to come over and see it."

So they trailed back over the deserted hall which Jean imagined to be peopled with rows of waiting humanity, past the long desk with the heavy files beyond, and into a room similar to the one they had just left, but from its far door came the sound of running water and a curl of steam, two signs which Jean was beginning to attach to the inevitable duty-room atmosphere.

And here it was again, with all the trappings of a miniature theatre.

"And that's about all there is to 'Out-patients' after the clinics are over," said Nurse Davis apologetically. "Having prepared everything, so that it only has to be laid out in the morning, our duties are more or less over—except for cutting extra dressings and packing them into drums to go to be baked. If there is an afternoon clinic we find there is little enough time in which to get all this finished, but to-day is our slack day . . . we should be studying, or . . . but Hunt was once a hairdresser and beauty expert, so she likes to practise her trade in her spare time."

"I'll say she does!" Norah laughed. "Do you remember those beauty parties?"

Their faces alight with merriment, they turned to Jean, starting together. "When we were on night-duty," they chorused, and then Norah stopped, allowing Davis to continue.

". . . we used to collect together in Hunt's room after we came off duty in the morning. Usually we had doughnuts or cakes of some sort, and a huge brown teapot which held enough for two or three cups all round; seven of us, there were.

"Then I washed hair, and Norah set it; Hunt plucked eyebrows and Jackie—Jackson, you know—performed miracles with hot towels and face-packs. Smithy turned manicurist."

"And so to bed," laughed Norah. "Usually we weren't ready for bed on those occasions until after midday, when Home-Sister would come round to find us putting the last crumbs out for the sparrows . . . I'd better let her peep into the X-ray and treatment rooms, hadn't I? Just here, Jean."

And Norah went through a door in the corner of the large hall.

"Now we're in the proper basement of the Hospital," she said. "That was a new wing. Here we are."

The room they had entered was large and rather gloomy, its four walls seeming to crouch back from the great hooded monster which dominated all.

That was the X-ray machine.

It stood in the centre of the room, and only after being led firmly up to it, Jean became aware that it was in fact just a long table; rather like the operating-table in the theatre upstairs. Over it stood a large frame which could be pulled up and down the table on side-runners, and to which the "hood" was fixed on a movable joint.

As Norah explained, the patient could lie on the table and have the frame arranged at the level that would enable the "hood" to be brought over the part to be X-rayed.

This "hood" was simply an external fitting, rather like a megaphone, which directed the rays on to the required part.

These rays, passing through the patient, met the X-ray film which fitted into the table below. The whole table was hollow so that a film could be placed under any portion of the patient that needed X-rayed.

And that is how any part of our body can be photographed.

It is necessary for the patient to get undressed to be X-rayed, in case there is any silk woven into her underclothes. The ray cannot penetrate silk, therefore a patient must only wear garments of cotton or wool, which should not be fastened with any pins, clips, or buttons, as the metal will show-up in the X-ray photograph.

For this reason every X-ray department has its own dressing-room, a little room opening off the main one, which Norah showed to Jean.

"All those dressing gowns are made of pure wool with woollen girdles," she said, "so if the patient is always dressed in *just* one of those, we are sure that nothing extra will be photographed.

"And here"—she led the way through a short corridor and into another room at the back of the X-ray room—"is the electrical treatment and mass-age department."

"One, two—and *lift* it up. Three, four, and slo-owly down," sang a musical voice. "Now again . . . no, rest a moment." For the woman in a white linen coat had caught sight of the visitors.

This time the room was long and narrow, and to Jean's amazement looked very like the gymnasium at school. Only in addition to the horizontal bars and the great "horse," were a row of couches, each with a pillow and two soft blankets.

Upon one of them lay a little girl.

Clad only in brief panties she lay on her back, wearing a look of deep concentration. Now her legs lay flat before her. A moment ago they had been weaving strange patterns in the air.

There was a peculiar smell in the air.

"Miss Wright, do you mind my bringing a young visitor in here?" asked Norah prettily. "She's inspecting our Hospital."

"Not at all . . . and I'm sure Jacqueline doesn't mind either. Do you Jackie?" The masseuse addressed the little figure on the couch while she gently stroked the thin legs. Jean was fascinated by her hands; they were strong and supple.

"No, I don't mind." A curly brown head popped up from the couch. "Would you like to see me do my exercises?"

"Yes, please," they answered.

"I'm good now, aren't I, Miss Wright? But I wasn't good once," Jackie added, as if to make up for her boasting. "I couldn't move them at all *once*, could I, Miss Wright?"

"No, dear, but they're better now. Jackie had an accident," Miss Wright explained.

"Yes, I remember," said Norah.

Jackie turned solemn eyes in her direction, and then her face was alight with recognition.

"Why you're Nurse Curlylocks who used to give me orange juice," she trilled joyously.

"And didn't you just *love* it," laughed Norah. She turned to Jean. "I was on the casualty ward when Jackie came in after her accident. She tried to jump out of a bedroom window, didn't you, Jackie? Thought she'd like to fly, I think."

"No," said Jackie firmly. "I *fell* . . . and both my legs were broken," she finished almost proudly.

"She thought Miss Wright hadn't got enough work to do, that's what it was. You see, Miss Wright specialises in broken limbs . . . she gets them working again. . . ."

". . . *after* Dr. Thomas has mended them with plaster," corrected Jackie, and then added, "Mine were hard to get working again, weren't they, Miss Wright? 'Cos they were both broken and one couldn't help the other."

"That's right." Miss Wright was smiling. "We had to work hard at first, hadn't we?"

Jean had noticed some clothes on the next couch, half-covered by a school blazer.

"Is she a patient *in* the hospital?" she inquired of Norah.

"Not now. You went home about a month ago, didn't you, Jackie?"

"More than a month now, but I used to come up every day for massage . . . now it's only twice a week, 'cos I do my exercises at home. Mummy leaves me here while she does her shopping. She'll be back in a moment."

"And we haven't done our new exercise yet," said Miss Wright briskly. "We always have a new one each week."

"Well, we'll be off. Good-bye, Jackie. Don't forget to come and see us in the ward sometime."

"Good-bye, Nurse Curlylocks."

As the door shut behind them, Jackie's new exercise was in progress.

"One, two . . . and lift . . . and *turn*. Three, four . . . now down again."

"Does Miss Wright have very many patients with broken limbs?" asked Jean.

"Yes. They all go to her to be taught to use them again. Often it's just like teaching a baby to walk. Of course they're mended by the time she gets them."

"What was the smell in there?"

"That was made by the various electric lamps with which she treats many of her patients. Didn't you see them standing in the corner?"

"Yes, I believe I did. Big silver things weren't they?"

"That's right. Jackie will have a few minutes of sun-ray when her exercises are finished. She's beginning to look brown, didn't you notice?"

"Yes. I thought perhaps she'd had a holiday."

"No, it's just the sun-ray lamp, but, of course, it

has the same effect in a few minutes as hours of sunshine."

They turned a corner in the dim basement and saw before them an open square of sunshine.

"Give me the real thing every time," said Norah as they sped towards it.

"Me, too," agreed Jean, sniffing the air laden with the smells of a summer garden.

CHAPTER SEVEN

THE NURSES' HOME

THEY were walking along a raised concrete path, under a corrugated iron roof, which was supported at intervals by wooden posts.

"Is this the covered way?" asked Jean.

"Yes, it takes us round by the back of the tennis court, and through the vegetable garden to the back of the Home," said Norah. "Why? Did you expect it to be built in?"

"Yes, I did."

"This is all that is really necessary. In wet weather the roof keeps us dry and although the rain may beat in on the path, it doesn't hold puddles as the gravel paths do, so we don't get wet feet. . . . Squiffy and Tops have gone in now, I expect."

The tennis court was silent, but as they passed the wire-fencing, two flannel-clad figures were intent on tightening up the net.

"That's the opposition taking over for a practice," said Norah, waving back as one of the men turned, and catching sight of her, raised his racket in a salutation.

"The R.M.O. and Simon Field," Norah told

Jean. "The one whom Nurse Tibbitts is engaged to, you know."

"Yes, I remember, but what does R.M.O. mean?"

"Just Resident Medical Officer. He's in charge of the housemen, who are fairly newly qualified. They are responsible to the various visiting surgeons and physicians, and take their orders from them, but the R.M.O. is always on the spot to help . . . oh! . . . he's coming over!"

Jean was surprised at the urgency of Norah's tone, but she greeted him with her usual light cheeriness as he reached the little covered path.

"Have you been watching our champions?" she rallied. "They've been dishing-up your medicine for next week. . . . Jean, this is Dr. Benson, our R.M.O., he's playing in the tournament next week." Her eyes were warmer than her easy tone as she turned to him. "And my cousin is viewing the Hospital."

"How d'you do? Hope she'll like it as much as we do . . . but, perhaps she couldn't . . . I mean, it's not the same when you don't know anyone, is it?"

Now what exactly does he *mean*, thought Jean. Because although he seemed a very cheery and altogether human young man, yet his tone was too fervent for his words. The same intensity was in his eyes, and Jean wondered if she could be just *imagining* that it was for Norah.

"What about a set?" he asked.

"I'm in uniform," answered Norah. So unlike *her*, to pass such an obvious remark, thought Jean.

"Well, couldn't you change?"

"I *could*."

Gracious, she was undecided. This was a new Norah.

"It wouldn't take long," he encouraged, ". . . and if your cousin would make a fourth?" Even if Jean *could* have resisted a tennis court, she could never have ignored his pleading eyes.

"Oh, I'd love to," she said—and it was really quite true.

He looked relieved.

"Very well, if you want to," Norah appeared to hesitate as she took Jean's blazer, but she was moving rapidly along the covered path as she flung it over her shoulder. "It's all right, I'll borrow a racket for you, Jean." She *can* run, thought Jean.

"You don't need to change, do you?" he asked. "Girls play tennis in those things don't they?" He motioned towards her gym tunic.

"Oh yes . . . and my shoes are rubber soled. They're a bit heavy, but they'll do for a hard court."

There was a moment's silence as he turned to watch Dr. Field. His gaze towards the net was intent yet unseeing.

There's something on his mind, thought Jean,

and I've a strong feeling that it's nothing to do with this game.

And then almost before Simon Field had joined them, Norah was back again, looking radiantly youthful in her crisp white shorts and open-necked blouse.

"Have I been long?" she asked, handing a racket to Jean.

"I didn't know a woman *could* be so quick . . . when it came to changing clothes," the R.M.O. answered. " . . . er, shall we split?" He dragged his gaze from Norah to look at Dr. Field for support. "What about it . . . do we toss?"

"No, Jean and I will play you two." Simon Field was quick to challenge him. "And they say St. Bride's turns out excellent tennis champions, so you'd better look out."

"Right, we'll risk it," and Dr. Benson piloted Norah to the far end of the court.

Then Jean settled down to enjoy her favourite sport. There was nothing more satisfying to her than the open flat of a tennis court and the "ping" of a ball against her racket.

"Phew! . . . I've backed a winner," said Dr. Field as he watched her first service with satisfaction.

It soon became evident that they *were* the winning pair, although the knowledge was not as thrilling as it might have been. Jean could feel no envy in the minds of the losing side. They, too, were playing their game and it had little or nothing to do with tennis.

The score mounted unequally, and Jean found herself being patted on the back by her partner.

"Well done. When are you going to play for St. Mary's?" he asked.

"Don't encourage her," warned Tim Benson, "you might find yourself on the wrong side of the net next time." He laughed ruefully. "They teach you good tennis at St. Bride's."

"Yes," answered Jean, "we're awfully keen on it there, but most of the courts are grass, so we suffer agonies of anxiety before tournaments in case the weather's all wrong. *This* is a good court!"

"Mm, but *are* you coming here . . . to be a nurse, I mean?" insisted Tim.

"Er, I—I haven't actually decided," answered Jean, wondering why on earth she didn't just say "no." After all, she had never even considered being a nurse, but I suppose I've got to be *something*, she told herself rather lamely, and immediately put the thought to the back of her mind.

"We're off for some tea," Norah was saying.

"Bread and jam?" asked Tim.

"No," she answered. "We're having a tea-party in my room . . . all sorts of lovely things, but *not* bread and jam."

"Aren't you going to invite us too?" he begged.

"What's the good," laughed Norah. "The Nurses'

Home would be in an uproar if I had a mixed-party. No, you'll have to wait until next week. We're giving a dance after the tournament. Maybe I'll invite you then. Good-bye, thanks for the set!"

"Make it a whole game next time," he called as they regained the covered path and moved off towards the Home.

The two doctors turned back on to the court as Norah and Jean disappeared into the vegetable plot near the back of the Home.

"Behold Robin's beloved kingdom!" sang Norah.

"Tomatoes!" cried Jean.

"Yes, and everything else it is possible to grow in this climate . . . especially carrots. There comes a time in the year when we seem to exist solely on carrots. We even have great trenches of them buried in straw to last through the winter. . . . This door leads straight into the nurses' cloakroom. I've left my cloak in the Hospital, but never mind, I can fetch it later."

They passed through a green door, and across a little red tiled passage and straight into a square room lined with wash-basins. Jean noticed the inevitable spotlessness which she was beginning to associate with any part of a hospital.

As they busily washed their hands, footsteps approached the door. It opened slowly as a figure in blue—another Sister, thought Jean—carefully manipulated two vases of rather faded flowers round the door before pulling the rest of herself after them.

"Jean, here is our Home Sister," announced Norah. "This is my cousin, Sister. She's come to have tea with me. May I show her all over the Home? She's seen the Hospital."

"Yes, do, Nurse. What a good thing we have fresh flowers for the sitting-rooms."

Leaving the vases on the scrubbed centre-table, she crossed to a small bin under one of the sinks, and deposited the faded flowers therein.

Now the door was opening again and a basket of lovely roses appeared, followed by another figure. This time it was a nurse.

"Just in time for our visitors, Nurse," welcomed Sister.

"Hallo," greeted Norah. "Jean, this is Nurse Watson our Home Nurse . . ."

". . . and my right hand," prompted Sister.

"How d'you do. What lovely roses!" said Jean breathlessly.

Nurse Watson held them forward for her to sniff. "They're for the sitting-rooms. Matron grows them in her own garden."

"That's the other side of the Hospital, so I'm afraid you didn't see it," apologised Norah. "We came out through O.P.D.," she explained to Sister, "all because we were in a hurry for our tea, and even now we haven't had it. We played tennis instead. This young thing's good too!" She nodded towards Jean.

"Yes, I saw you," remarked Nurse Watson. "The R.M.O. wasn't in frightfully good form, was he?" she added smilingly.

Norah blushed, and changed the subject.

"Mind you arrange those roses nicely. I'll take Jean into the lecture-room first so you *might* put them in the sitting-room before we get there," she hinted.

"If you don't run away and leave me in peace, to arrange them, they'll fade before ever I get the chance," threatened Sister darkly, but her eyes followed Norah warmly as she ushered Jean out of the door in mock terror.

They were in the main corridor of the Home. Jean remembered walking along it just over two hours ago.

"You'd better peep into the rooms down here first," said Norah, "and then we'll go up for tea and I'll show you a typical bedroom corridor. They're all the same. . . . Here's the lecture-room."

And there were rows and rows of chairs facing a raised dais. Behind the dais, the wall was fitted with a large blackboard. Just like ours at school, thought Jean. Then as Norah pressed a switch the whole board was lit up by a long lamp fitted at the top of it.

"And this is for our lantern lectures," she announced, pulling a cord, and so releasing the spring of a white blind, which fell down over the blackboard.

Jean had noticed the big black projector standing at the back of the hall.

"Do you often have lantern lectures?" she asked enviously, because she only remembered having seen two at school. One had been of big-game hunting in Central Africa, and the other of a party who climbed Mount Everest. They had been great fun.

"Yes, quite often," answered Norah. "This hall is for the senior nurses who attend lectures given by the visiting surgeons and physicians. The juniors take most of their lectures in the P.T.S.—Preliminary Training School—but I'll show you that later."

"What sort of pictures do they show you, though?" asked Jean curiously.

"Last time a famous plastic-surgeon came and gave us a lecture on his work in the last war. That was the beginning of plastic-surgery as we know it to-day. He showed us pictures of people who had been disfigured by gunshot."

"Ugh—awful!" Jean shuddered.

"Not really," said Norah consolingly. "Because at the same time he showed us how they had been marvellously repaired to look like new faces."

"Is that what *plastic*-surgery means . . . sort of *patching* people?"

"That's right. You've heard of skin-grafting, haven't you? That's just the same as any other sort of grafting; trees and flowers and things. It's taking a piece of *living* material and joining, or grafting it on to another living thing, so that the two become one. It is done with bones and muscle, as well as skin."

"How . . . bones, I mean, how *can* you?"

"Well, there was one picture that this surgeon showed us of a man who had lost his nose, but a piece of rabbit bone covered with a skin flap from his own forehead made him a lovely new one."

"*Rabbit* bone!"

"Why not? Although these days surgeons seem to favour a little piece of the patient's own rib."

"But what happens if they haven't got anything to replace the rib with?"

"Nothing," said Norah airily. "A rib or two aren't missed unless you want to go in for a boxing career. The ribs *are* meant to act as a shield for your heart and lungs, but you would have to be pretty well knocked about for it to matter if an odd one was missing."

"It must have been a jolly interesting lecture then."

"It *was*," agreed Norah, as they closed the door of the lecture-room. "More than that," she added as she led the way down the corridor. "It makes one so glad to feel that a person who once upon a time would have lived the life of an outcast, can now face the world again. People are not awfully kind to the unfortunate ones who have a facial deformity . . . and children stare so."

"Mm," Jean agreed, wondering uncomfortably how many times, as a little girl, she had pulled her mother's sleeve saying, "Look, Mummy, at that funny lady over there!"

"Here is the junior sitting-room," announced Norah.

"Ooh . . . lovely!" said Jean.

The room was low and square. *Cool*, Jean thought. She could smell again the lovely summer scents as the green cretonne curtains were wafted towards her by a breeze from the open windows.

Two of the four windows opened on to the veranda. The other two had deep, white window-seats, cushioned with the green cretonne. A centre-table already held some of Matron's roses.

"I must try the piano," said Jean, and she noticed the softness of the deep green carpet as she moved towards the baby-grand.

Norah's eye was held for a moment by the open magazines and pieces of sewing that littered the chair.

"Untidy little beasts," she said good-humouredly, as she moved to pick up a book which had fallen from the writing-desk.

"Where are they?" asked Jean.

"Gone to tea, I should think. It's nearly five; the ones who are off duty this evening will be back again at any moment. These young things"—she pointed to the open books—"have probably had a free afternoon. They go to four o'clock tea and return to their wards at half past so that others can come off-duty for the rest of the day. Come and see *our* room now."

It was next door.

"Isn't it huge," gasped Jean.

"Mm, that's because it's built as a ballroom. We have our concerts and dances in here, because there's room for a stage to be put up . . . and if we can't always have a band, we've got our radio-gram. . . . Hello, Blackie! Been to tea?"

"No, not going," answered a figure from the depths of a pink-flowered couch. "It's too hot for bread and jam. I'm feeling delicate."

"Come and have some with us then. I'm showing my young cousin over the Hospital—at least, we've seen that, and now we're touring the Home. What time are you on duty?"

"Not till six o'clock to-day."

"Good," said Norah promptly. "There's time for tea in my room. Jean and I are having it there, so do come."

"Thanks, I'd love to." She turned to Jean, waving an airy hand over the sitting-room. "Not bad, is it?"

"I think it's grand," Jean's tone was enthusiastic. "I love your window-seats, and cretonne covers always look so cool. I suppose your carpet doesn't fit to the wall because of dancing."

"That's right; we roll it out of the way on those occasions. Then all these armchairs are put out into the wide corridor and sheltered discreetly with screens and a few palms. There sit the lazy ones, while this becomes a ballroom. We keep the small chairs for the wallflowers . . . only there aren't any, usually."

"Now come upstairs," prompted Norah, "and we'll put the kettle on to boil in the pantry, while I show you a bedroom corridor." She led them out of the sitting-room towards the main staircase.

"Isn't there a dining-room?" asked Jean anxiously.

"Of course there is. Good gracious, I nearly forgot."

And in almost less time than it takes to say it, Norah had marshalled her back towards the front of the Home, and down a little side passage towards a double swing-door. There was no need to open it. Jean could see the groups of small tables through the glass panels of the door.

"I imagined it would be one long table, like at school," she remarked.

"Oh no. You see with long tables it automatically happens that the seniors sit at the top and the juniors at the bottom. That makes a sort of class distinction. But here we just fill up the little tables as we come in, and so when we are *off duty* we are ' all girls together,' so to speak. There's quite enough professional etiquette in the wards where it *is* necessary, without dragging it into the Home, where it isn't. . . . Notice the hot plate?"

"Just like Lyons."

"Built after their style, I believe. Home Sister and her assistant nurse serve out the meals from there, and the dining-room maids distribute it. We usually pour out our own tea. . . . Here's Squiffy! Did you have a good game?" Norah asked as one of the nurses left her table and strolled out of the door.

" Yes, not at all bad: Tops is in good form."

"The opposition is in training at the moment," warned Norah.

"They're welcome; they'll need it for some of Top's backhanders," announced Squiffy airily. "See you at supper, Brownie!" and she disappeared in the direction of the senior common-room.

"Now . . . *tea!*" Norah headed once more for the staircase.

On the third floor of the Home, they paused, panting.

"I'm not going to apologise for dragging you all the way here," she informed them. "It's worth it. Home Sister has offered me a room on the first floor but I prefer this. It's airy, and see"—she paused by the landing-window—"there's a lovely view."

From here, the Hospital grounds lay before them. The window overlooked the orchard, flower-beds and the tennis court, on which two figures ran backwards and forwards after a ball too small and swift to be seen. Beyond the Hospital, the hill sloped down between pastureland to the river with the little town of Rivacre huddled on its banks. The hills in the farther distance were lost amongst the heat-haze.

"Shall I put the kettle on, while you show her this corridor?" asked Nurse Black obligingly.

"Thanks, Blackie, but I shall have to show her the pantry. I'd be awfully obliged if you'd set the tea though. Here's my keys." Norah hauled them out of a pocket beneath her apron. "And there's biscuits and cakes in a tin in the cupboard over my wardrobe. All the china is there, too. . . . Come on, Jean, here's the pantry."

As Blackie sped down the corridor towards Norah's bedroom, Jean was led into a little room by the top of the stairs. A sink, an empty china cupboard, and an electric kettle were its only contents.

"This cupboard usually contains a little store of tea and sugar and some china," explained Norah, "but most of us have our own as well, just in case we find the cupboard bare. And each of us has her favourite bedtime beverage and a personal tea caddy."

"But they *do* give you all your meals in the dining-room, don't they?" asked Jean.

"Oh yes. But nurses are famous for their thirst for tea. Besides it *is* necessary to be able to have a hot drink before you go to bed, especially on night-duty. The last meal in the morning is after you come off duty, at 9 a.m. Most of us don't go to bed until midday, so as to be sure of sleeping until the evening; so you can imagine that tea and biscuits are an attraction just before we retire for the day."

"It *must* be funny to live all topsy-turvy like that," Jean ruminated aloud as she followed Norah through a second doorway.

"Our laundry-room," announced Norah. "No, we *don't* have to wash all our clothes and we *have* got a Hospital laundry," she added, answering Jean's unspoken questions. "But, you see, we do like to wash our own smalls—the better ones any-how. We feel we can treat them more gently in a home atmosphere, and after all they are expensive to replace.

"So here, everything is to hand, sink, drying-rack, ironing board—and most precious of all—*an electric iron*. What we'd ever do without it, I just don't know, if it ever wore out. . . . Now the bath-rooms." On the other side of the staircase, two similar doors led into the bathrooms.

"Nothing very unusual about them," Norah remarked, "but they *do* provide really hot water at any hour of the day or night. And that, too, is really a necessity in a Hospital. We can have lovely baths."

"How many people have to use these bathrooms?" asked Jean.

"Fourteen. That's only seven per bath. It could be a lot worse. I've never had to wait for very long. There are fourteen nurses on each floor you see . . . and that's all . . . oh, except this."

She opened another door, and Jean peeped in at a sink, a large bin and a tall thin stove. "What's that?" she inquired.

"Just an incinerator," answered Norah. "There's one on each floor. It eats up any amount of rubbish that is no good for salvage. The maids use this little cupboard for washing their dusters and so on. . . . Now, tea!"

Jean was looking forward to sitting down for a while. What large places hospitals are, she thought, as Norah led her through an open door, and there was one of the prettiest bedrooms Jean had ever seen.

Cream paint and blue cretonne . . . and Blackie reclining in a cushioned chair welcoming them towards a round table daintily laid with blue china.

Jean tried not to stare too hard at the chocolate

cake, but she had eaten an early lunch, and seemed to have done so many things since then.

"Don't move, Blackie, Jean can have this chair with a cushion on it," said Norah, pulling forward a small bedside-chair, and snatching one of the cushions from the divan. "I'll use the bed," she added.

Blackie was struggling to her feet. "I'll slip along to the pantry and make the tea," she said. "That kettle ought to be boiled by now."

"No, you sit down and entertain Jean. I'll do it," and Norah vanished with the teapot and a little blue tin tucked underneath her arm.

Then Blackie very firmly took Jean and planted her in the comfy armchair.

"I've been sitting all afternoon," she said, "and I know what it is to walk slowly round a place as large as St. Mary's. Not to mention tennis on top of it."

"Thank you, I *am* rather tired," admitted Jean, as she snuggled happily into the blue cretonne. "There's such a lot to think about, too," she added.

"There is indeed, and it's worth a second thought," agreed Nurse Black as she carefully removed her shoes and settled herself on a corner of the divan.

CHAPTER EIGHT

A CHATTY HALF-HOUR

JEAN eyed the last piece of chocolate cake on the plate and shook her head sadly. Three pieces had exhausted her cake-eating capacity. "Me, too," said Norah.

She laughed across at Blackie. "Do you remember the chocolate cake we made in the P.T.S.?"

Blackie took breath for a deep sigh, and lost it again in a ripple of mirth. "Do I!" she gasped, and added for Jean's benefit. "We covered it with custard and ate it as a pudding . . . the effect was heavy, to say the least!"

"Tell me more about the P.T.S.," Jean begged. "That's where you learn to cook isn't it?"

Norah left her little chair and curled herself on the other end of the divan. "Go on, Blackie, this is your innings. I'll sit back and prompt you if you forget anything."

Blackie stretched her legs with a deep sigh and then curled them up again before replying. "Mm . . . it's difficult to know where to begin . . . but if you want to hear about *cookery*, there was once a Shrove Tuesday . . ."

A movement on the other end of the divan made Jean look over towards where Norah was shaking in silent mirth.

Blackie continued remorselessly ". . . when Brownie invited a few visitors to a kitchen pancake-party. Part of the show was the tossing, of course, and Brownie, being bent on tossing hers higher than any one's, flung a half-cooked pancake right against the ceiling. There it stuck. Lord, what a moment! It was quite impossible to get it down. So *there* it stayed. Every morning for weeks we greeted Sister in fear and trembling. We expected it to be noticed, but time went on and still the pancake remained glued to the kitchen ceiling over the gas-stove. Eventually it collected so much dirt that it looked like a round stain on the white-wash."

"But didn't *anyone* see it?" asked Jean breathlessly.

"No, the ceilings are very high in the P.T.S. kitchen. It wasn't found until the spring-cleaning, by which time no one could tell what it was meant to be. They had a vague suspicion that it was a sort of plaster left over from the painters of the year before. Lucky for us . . . wasn't it, Brownie?"

"Yes," said Norah, doubtfully, "but you know I've always had a feeling that Sister guessed what it was and didn't want to say. It would have meant a cross-examination of every nurse in the P.T.S. and I think she preferred to leave it as another of the unsolved mysteries of the Hospital. There are enough of them, goodness only knows . . . but this isn't going to be another one. . . ." She jumped from the divan towards the window.

The sound of many voices had been gathering force while Norah spoke and they had now reached a screaming pitch.

Together the three girls crowded into the little window-frame, and looked down on to the scene below them.

Norah's bedroom was above a part of the sitting-room, and overlooked the veranda and the lawns. Now the veranda was covered with white-linen figures all wearing the handkerchief cap of a probationer.

One of them had climbed upon a little rustic table and from there she addressed her confederates, who almost drowned her speech in their hilarious laughter.

"Ssh . . ." the mounted probationer grew impatient, ". . . how on earth can I give you any idea what it's to be about if you won't just *listen* to me. This is serious. Are we going to show the seniors what we're made of, or aren't we?"

" *We are!* " The chorus was unanimous.

"Very well, then. *Listen to your parts.*"

Norah nearly fell out of the window in her efforts to get at them. "The idiots," she hissed. "Every one can hear them. Hey!" she shouted. "You'd better go somewhere else to practise. Half the Hospital can hear you."

And indeed from nearly every window of the Home peered a white-linen covered head.

The upturned faces from the veranda looked imploringly at Norah's window. "We need somewhere *big*," beseeched their leader, "and the sitting-room's full."

"Well, try the badminton-room," encouraged Norah. "Ask Home Sister for the keys."

"Thanks, we will." The leader gave orders for her followers to join her in the badminton-room and moved off towards the french windows leading into the Home.

"They've started early," said Norah, turning away from the window.

"Started? What *was* it all about?" asked Jean, in wonderment.

"They're practising for the autumn concerts," explained Norah. "Each year of nursing students performs a separate act and we are each supposed to keep it a secret from the others, so that there's an element of surprise on the concert night."

"Will you be doing anything?"

"'Spect so. Have you thought of anything yet, Blackie?" asked Norah. "We can't let the little beggars show us up. Wonder what they're doing, though," she finished thoughtfully.

"Something *tremendous*, I expect," said Blackie.

"It's funny how the first year probationers always think they'll do something on the *Hiawatha* scale just to show the full extent of their talent. Do you remember when we did *Romeo and Juliet?*"

". . . and the balcony gave way!" laughed Norah. "Could I possibly forget it? Do you happen to remember that *I* was poor Juliet?" She turned to Jean. "Did I ever tell you about that?

"It was my first year in Hospital and we were all so excited about the concerts. We have them during the autumn because of the long dark evenings when we can't go out—or at least there isn't much to do if we do go out. There was Blackie, Jackson, Smith, Tibbins, Squiffy and Tops and myself; we were all very new to Hospital life.

"Most of us had come straight from College and wanted to show what we were worth, so we decided to develop a Shakespearian repertoire. *Romeo and Juliet* was our first effort in that direction, and, as Juliet, I stood on a ladder behind a screen and reacted to the love-songs of my Romeo— Squiffy in a pair of navy gym-knickers and a wooden sword. Everything was fine—well, not bad you know—until my ladder started creaking. Squiffy sang louder and louder but the awful creaks filtered through to the audience. I think maybe I began to wear an anxious expression; so would you, Blackie, if you'd been standing on that ladder.

"Anyhow, the audience began to find more humour in the situation than seemed to be kind to the actors, until, at last, amid an awful howl of mirth, the ladder, screen and I collapsed!

"A good time was had by all but we fell out with Mr. Shakespeare. We tackled something a little less ambitious after that."

"We've had more fun with those concerts than with any other activity during my training," gasped Blackie as she straightened her countenance again. "Some of the acts have been pretty good though, haven't they? D'you remember . . . there I am at it again. I promise you, Jean, that from now on I will not encourage your cousin to *remember* anything. It must be most annoying to be in the company of two people who are continually harping on their combined experiences."

"Oh, but it isn't," Jean expostulated. "I love hearing it. I'm learning *lots* about hospital life. Much more than Norah's ever told me," she finished, flashing an accusing glance towards her cousin.

"That," said Norah, excusing herself, "is because I try not to talk too much about Hospital when I get out of a nurse's uniform. As a tribe we are inclined to talk too much 'shop' and I must say, people encourage us. Nothing goes down better than a nice little hospital story."

"Tell me some then . . . tell me about night-duty," Jean begged Blackie anxiously.

"All right," Blackie soothed her. "I'll tell you about night-duty."

"D'you remember, Brownie? We had been itching to go on night-duty for weeks before our turn came, and then one morning Snookums—that's night-sister, who always takes a breakfast roll-call—said, ' The Nurses Black and Brown to go to bed at 2 p.m. to-day and report for night-duty to-night.' Magic words!

"Nine o'clock that night found us both waiting breathlessly outside Matron's office. Which ward was it to be? Would we be together? The formal announcement came. ' Nurse Black and Nurse Brown will both report to St. Andrew's ward. Nurse Brown will take the position of senior probationer. . . ."

". . . only because I'd been in the Hospital exactly one week longer than Blackie," announced Norah from her old position on the divan.

"Anyhow, it was a relief to know that we were to be together," continued Blackie. "We vowed never to move a step without each other.

"Hand in hand we approached St. Andrew's. The heavy door of the ward-corridor thumped behind us. . . ."

"Funny how that thump affects you differently in different stages of your career," broke in Norah. "At first it means ' got you; no escape,' then it means ' here again,' but eventually it grows to mean much more. Now I feel 'home again' whenever I hear a ward-door thump behind me. A feeling of 'this is *my* ground, I know every creak and sigh of it—it needs me.' When you get to that stage, nursing isn't a grind any more," she finished thoughtfully.

Blackie chuckled. "By then it's jolly well 'got you,' my girl, and only one thing'll 'pull you out.'"

"What's that?" breathed Jean.

"Marriage. But, wait a minute. We were talking about night-duty in St. Andrew's. *The door thumped behind!* We had entered a new world," she announced dramatically.

"I know. I know." Jean jabbered her agreement. "It was just like that to-day when Norah took me on to Mercy Ward and the door thumped and somebody was calling for a nurse. It gave me the creeps. Of course, that was before I'd seen any of them—the patients, I mean."

"Well, it's worse at night," Blackie said discouragingly. "There's a warm smell of almost everything under the sun—mostly disinfectants of course—but all bound up with something more intimate. The whole atmosphere is confined . . . and sort of . . . *hopeless*."

"Oh, dear," gasped Jean.

Norah was laughing. "Blackie, you are *awful*. You're making her wish she'd never asked you. You know we *loved* night-duty."

"I know we did," Blackie agreed, "but that was

just the feeling I had for at least a year whenever I walked on a ward-corridor at night, and she might as well know the worst first.

"Anyhow, it's easily explained," she continued unperturbed. "During the day there is so much activity in a hospital that the patients don't really have much time to think of their afflictions. Everything is new to them and they become interested in the mechanism of it all.

"Then in the quiet of the night comes a fear of this unknown quantity—their disease. How will it affect them? Does it mean that they will not be able to do all the things in life for which they had planned? They lie in the semi-darkness thinking of what they would be doing if they were at home, and—well, you know what it's like to be homesick."

Jean nodded, as Blackie continued.

"All that is the 'hopelessness' that I for one always felt in the atmosphere of a ward at night. It was always there making itself felt in the heavy sighs and coughs; and the sound of restless bodies turning. Now it doesn't seem hopeless any more because I know what to do about it."

"What do you do?" inquired Jean anxiously.

"I just creep round from bed to bed. At first the beds are holding unknown shapes. They even frightened me at first . . . goodness knows what I expected them to do to me. Then I found that the first one was called Mrs. Allen and she kept a fruit shop and was worrying in case she wouldn't be home in time for her daughter's wedding.

"Immediately she ceased to be a strange figure in a dim bed. She was a woman with a daughter. There was nothing so very unfamiliar about that.

"And so every dim form in the half-lit ward becomes a personality. A night-nurse gets to know even more of their lives than a day-nurse who has less time in which to chat to them. So you come on duty at night, knowing that there are people waiting to chat to you and that their comfort for the night depends on your help: perhaps just a hot drink, and a new arrangement of pillows or sometimes a tablet to take away the pain. The feeling that they are waiting for you is welcoming. That is what Brownie means when she says that the door thumps ' home again.'"

"Yes, I see, and what do you do when they are all asleep?" pressed Jean.

"Well, as there are quite a number of patients— an average of twenty—for a night-nurse to tuck down, they take some time to finish."

"Do you have to look after twenty people all by yourself?" Jean was amazed.

"Oh no, not in most hospitals. But in many of them—including here—there is one senior night-nurse to two juniors. As the day-staff have finished all the ward treatment there isn't supposed to be a lot to do to the patients, except encourage them to sleep. So the senior nurse goes round encouraging while the juniors get on with the hundred and one odd routine jobs."

"Cleaning again?" asked Jean.

"Some cleaning, I'm afraid, but not so much as there used to be. That doesn't mean that there is less to do though. It simply means that the juniors can graduate to some more interesting and instructive work. They pack the drums and . . ."

"Whatever does that mean?" interrupted Jean.

"Didn't you notice any drums in the duty-room when you were in the Hospital?"

"I—I—don't think . . ."

"Yes, you did, Jean," Norah interrupted her. "The tall silver boxes that I told you held sterile gauze and cotton wool for dressing wounds."

"Oh, yes I remember . . . and you mustn't put your hand inside them."

"That's right," laughed Blackie. "And so, of course, that is just what a new nurse always does the first time she is asked to get anything out of a drum. At least I know I did."

"And me," said Norah. "And old Tommy— that was my first ward-sister—said, ' Now you may put that back and take the drum right away and bring me a fresh one from the duty-room.' I felt awful!"

"Yes, and when you *do* realise that you should pick out the wool and gauze with forceps, you find the jolly old things hard to manipulate and probably touch the edge of the drum with a piece of wool on the way out," Blackie added ruefully.

"Then d'you have to get another drum?" asked Jean.

"Oh no; because you haven't put any germs inside the drum. You've only dirtied the one piece of wool you were meant to pick out. So only that piece has to be discarded."

"What a waste of good wool!" Jean was becoming salvage conscious.

"Oh no, it can be packed into the next empty drum, and go to be sterilised. That is what I meant when I said that the night nurses 'packed the drums.'"

"Oh, I see. What else do they do?"

"Sometimes they clean some instruments and iron any bandages that have been washed. Then, when all the patients are asleep—usually by midnight— they all have their midnight meal."

"And after that?"

"Well, sometimes there might be a patient who has woken up and needs some attention. Anyway a night-nurse should creep round her beds frequently to make sure that no one is lying awake waiting for her to come to them."

"But doesn't that wake them up—somebody walking round I mean?" Jean asked.

"It shouldn't if you wear quiet shoes. Some of

us like to wear leather pumps. Rubber makes a noise on the polished floors."

"Do you walk round all night?" Jean asked faintly.

"Oh no, there is usually a little shaded lamp in the ward and we can sit by that and arrange its shade so that a small pool of light falls on to our knitting, reading, or whatever we have chosen to do.

"You see, a night-nurse is often on duty for eleven hours at a time and during that time has no official 'off duty.' So while the patients are sleeping she is usually allowed to get on with any personal work—such as letter-writing—but, of course, if she is needed for anything else all that must be put to one side. If the patients wake up they can see her as she sits under the little light."

"It sounds easier than day-duty," Jean remarked.

"Hm, I wouldn't say that. You've got the morning to face."

"Why, what happens then?"

"Washing the patients, bed-making, breakfasts . . ."

At that moment a clamour of girlish voices broke the stillness of the corridor outside Norah's room.

"The P.T.S. are out," announced Norah mysteriously.

"And I shall be late on duty if I don't go," said Blackie, hurriedly rising and smoothing her apron with one hand as she pushed a straying curl under her cap with the other.

"Thanks for the tea, Brownie, and I hope I've told Jean some of what she wants to know. Good-bye, Jean; perhaps I'll be seeing you again some time." And with a rustle of her apron Blackie was gone.

"And we must be moving, too, if you want to see the P.T.S. before I send you home." Norah uncurled herself from the divan.

"What does P.T.S. actually stand for . . . of course I know what it *is*?"

"The Preliminary Training School, but I'll tell you more about it when you see it. Come on."

Norah led her out of the pretty little bedroom. "I'll clear up that later," she said, with a backward glance at the remnants of their tea-party.

CHAPTER NINE

THE P.T.S.

SISTER TUTOR met them at the entrance to the little wing of the Nurse's Home that was her domain.

"This is where we hatch our nurses," she announced when Norah had introduced her to Jean.

"Do you have to teach people . . . people, well— er—just like me, who don't know anything about nursing, that is?" Jean asked in surprise.

Sister Tutor smiled down at her. "Yes, just like you will be in another year or so, when you've finished school and got your school certificate."

"Can't you be a nurse without a school certificate?"

"Yes, you *can*, but we prefer to choose girls who can pass examinations fairly well because there is a certain amount of studying to be done, and if a nurse finds that difficult, it will make her training doubly hard. So if you haven't a school certificate most Matrons require you to pass an entrance examination. It all depends which Hospital you hope to enter, of course."

As Sister Tutor spoke she led them into a room which looked like any of the form-rooms at Jean's school. Cupboards lined the far wall.

"This is our little lecture-room," announced Sister. "During the first ten weeks of their training period, my pupils cover the ground work of anatomy, physiology, nursing, first-aid and hygiene. So, as you can imagine, they are pretty busy.

"At the end of that time they revise what they have learned and I examine them on those subjects.

"So, by the time they enter the Hospital as a probationer nurse, they have the foundation on which to build their experience.

"Of course, we don't limit the preliminary training period to book-learning. We have a small ' ward ' of our own, too . . . but let me show you this first."

She moved across to the cupboards and Jean followed. As Sister Tutor opened the first cupboard door, Jean gasped.

For out of the cupboard popped a whole skeleton.

"Meet Jimmy," laughed Sister as she saw the surprise on Jean's face. She went on to explain. "He's attached to a spring which is released as the door opens."

"He's not *really* a skeleton, is he?" Jean asked faintly. "I mean, he wasn't ever alive, was he?"

"Indeed he was. He was Mr. James Brown, who particularly requested that his bones should be used for instruction. So they are."

"That was awfully k-kind of him," stammered Jean, suppressing her shudders.

"Yes, wasn't it," Sister agreed. "So after his bones were cleaned and dried they were strung together on wire. Now he hangs in his cupboard and pops out for our anatomy lessons. Just think what good work he does."

"Isn't he made of *lots* of bones," remarked Jean. She moved cautiously over towards the swaying Jimmy and looked more carefully at his many parts.

"Yes," agreed Sister. "There are more than two hundred bones in the human body, and each has its special function . . . but perhaps you'll be learning about that one day."

"Yes . . . perhaps I will," Jean was surprised to hear herself say. But after all, why not? It would be exciting to become a nurse. In a Hospital something vital always seemed to be happening. Perhaps . . . But there was plenty of time in which to think about that.

Sister was saying, ". . . and this is our ward," as she led them through some glass doors and into a bright square room which held something of the polished brightness of a ward duty-room.

"You see, we do all our ' practical ' nursing tuition in here," she was explaining. "So we must have the apparatus of a ward, duty-room and sluice combined. Let me introduce you to our ' patients.'"

And there in a cot, just like the ones she had seen in St. Anne's ward, Jean saw a large baby-doll in a long flannel nightgown. "And everything else a baby requires," announced Sister proudly, turning up the nightgown to show the pinned diaper beneath.

"Oh!" Jean started back. She had turned to the full-sized bed beside the cot and met the gaze of its occupant. "Good gracious! It almost looks alive!"

"You mean Mrs. Smith," laughed Norah. "We sometimes used to think that she *was* alive, didn't we, Sister?"

"*Dear* Mrs. Smith," said Sister with a hint of laughter behind the gravity of her tone. "She is never so 'alive' as when we are trying to pretend that she's unconscious."

"When she *will* behave like a Jack-in-the-box," said Norah ruefully, as she laid back the bedclothes and started to fix the "limbs" of a full-sized, adult "doll." "But we can do most things with her, can't we, Sister?"

"Do you pretend she's a patient?" asked Jean.

"That's right. We wash her and bandage her in every conceivable way. Then we pretend she has a certain complaint and proceed to make her bed in the most suitable way for the particular illness we have given her. Sometimes she has a *dreadful* pain in her tummy, and a little while later she has lost her leg in an accident, and then—just for a change— we knock her down by a bus and fracture her skull.

"All those afflictions need a different arrangement of the bedclothes, so that keeps us busy for a long while. We have plenty of other toys to play with, too."

Sister turned to a big trolley, and Jean saw upon it the large silver drums and, on a glass-shelf above, the inevitable array of small instruments in shining jars of disinfectants. There, too, was the big steam steriliser—only *not* as big as the ones she had seen in the theatre—and by them a big round silver shining thing in the wall. Jean couldn't think what it was, but it was as big as one of her bicycle wheels and had a lever at each side and a pedal below.

"The bed-pan washer," explained Sister, noticing her puzzled gaze. "They are a comparatively new invention, but we have had them installed in all the sluices of our Hospital."

She placed a foot on the pedal, at the same time tweaking a handle on the front of the washer. The whole front pulled down on its hinges. Jean looked down a deep porcelain well.

Then taking an enamel bed-pan from the rack above, Sister placed it into the hollow of the heavy front-piece, and shut it all up again. When the apparatus was in its former closed condition, she locked it by releasing her foot from the pedal.

"Now, you see," she expounded. "I press first the cold-water lever, and then, if I think I require a high pressure, I can press the hot-water lever too." She promptly did so.

From the noise of the swiftly-rushing water inside the washer, Jean could tell that the pressure was indeed high.

"Those can be left running for as long as the nurse thinks it will be necessary," said Sister, "but not forgetting what a crime it is to waste water, of course," she added hastily.

"And lastly, we turn off the cold lever and leave the hot running for a few moments so that the bedpan is warm for further use. This rack, too, is a hot-water pipe," she explained as she took out the bedpan and, after carefully drying it with a gaily-coloured towel which hung by, she placed it back into the rack. "So, the pans are always kept warm."

Jean was fascinated. A heavy cloud of doubt had rolled away before her eyes.

As she turned away to look for new signs of instruction she nearly fell over a high stool which stood with others along a heavy bench. "A laboratory!" she exclaimed, for there were the familiar tripods, Bunsen burners, and other paraphernalia of the "stinks" at school.

"Just a small one," said Sister, opening a glass cupboard to show-off their array of lotions and crystals. "A nurse has to have some knowledge of chemistry, as she must be able to test certain fluids for any impurities. Many of the girls don't know anything at all about it when they come here. But that, too, is included in their preliminary training. Of course, they are only supposed to do the simple tests that can be judged with the naked eye. Microscopic tests are performed in the big Hospital laboratory.

"Here is more of our equipment. . . ." Sister moved towards a large cupboard, fitting all the way across the top of the room by the door. Opening the doors she brought to view some rows of shelves on which stood groups of enamel bowls, jugs, and trays, arrays of rubber tubing and an assortment of cardboard boxes. The latter were labelled mysteriously with such names as "Higginson's Syringe," "Catheters," "Nelson's Inhaler" and lots more names equally unheard-of by Jean.

"The pupils learn how to prepare trays for various treatments," explained Sister, "so that by the time they go on to the wards they are familiar with the instruments they will find there. They know how each instrument must be cleaned and stored for further use. You see," she pointed to an upper shelf, "some of them have to be kept sterile for immediate use, and they are stored in a suitable lotion instead of in a box."

"Oh yes, Norah showed me," Jean exclaimed. "I saw them in one of the Hospital duty-rooms."

"That's right," Sister replied. "They become old friends after a while. You meet them wherever you go in a hospital . . . oh, and the lotions, of course . . ." She opened another door.

"The big bottles are the lotions." Norah directed Jean's gaze to the bottom of the cupboard where stood some huge bottles of the pink and mauve lotion that Jean had seen before.

"We call those *very* large bottles 'Winchesters,'" Norah added.

"However much do they hold?"

"Half a gallon, don't they, Sister?" Norah inquired.

"They are twice as big as a quart-bottle of milk."

"How lovely and clean they all look," remarked Jean.

"That's because we use them carefully," replied Sister proudly.

"*Always pour out your lotion away from the label,*" Norah chanted naughtily.

"And a very good rule, too," laughed Sister.

"Why?" Jean couldn't see the point of their remarks.

"Because as you are pouring it, a few drops may be lost down the side of the bottle. Many of these lotions would stain the label which cannot be washed like the glass on the other side of the bottle. In time, as you can imagine, it might become impossible to read the name of the lotion on the label. That would be dangerous, perhaps. Hence the rule ' always pour out your lotion *away* from the label'!"

By now, Jean's eyes had caught sight of another novelty. There at the top of the cupboard sat a row of saucy little bottles with flannel frills round their necks.

"Whatever for," she gurgled.

"Read the labels," instructed Sister.

Jean did so. "Liquid paraffin, Castor-oil—ugh! Glycerine, Almond-oil, Glycerine and Borax . . ." she trailed off wonderingly.

"Don't you see, they're all sticky," said Sister. "If a drop trickled down the side of the bottle each time you used them, in no time the bottles would be nasty to handle. The flannel frills are there to catch the drips."

"Not that even *they* are left alone to grapple with the situation," interrupted Norah. "All these bottles are wiped with a soapy cloth and dried at least once a week, but the frills save them needing such treatment more often than we can give it."

Sister was closing the cupboard door when Jean asked, "Are any of them poisonous?"

"Yes, but not dangerously so," Sister assured her. "You may have noticed that many of the bottles had 'For External Use Only' on their labels. Well, they wouldn't be good to drink, but if you *did* try, they are more likely to make you sick than anything else. Besides, no one would be so silly. They taste horrid. Some of them are harmless and the others are so diluted that it wouldn't be easy to drink enough to do any real harm.

"There has been a special Act of Parliament

passed for safeguarding dangerous drugs. They have to be locked in a cupboard of their own. Various precautions are taken about the key to the D.D. cupboard—as we call it—but most ward-sisters keep it on their person. When they go off-duty they pass it on to the nurse who will be in charge of the ward during their absence. . . . And *now* I think you have seen all our ' ward.' Now for our kitchen. . . ."

Sister led them out of the ward and across the corridor. Norah smiled across at Jean as they followed her. "Didn't you expect all this?" she asked as she noticed the bewildered expression on her young cousin's face.

"No, I certainly didn't. I just thought . . . well . . . I don't know that I'd *ever* thought so much trouble was taken to show people how to nurse."

"Dash it all, we *do* call ourselves a profession," chided Norah good-naturedly, as she followed Jean into the kitchen.

Here again were deep cupboards along one end of the room. At the other end there stood three sinks, each with hot and cold-water taps and draining-boards. Three gas stoves stood by the door and in the centre of the room was a huge bare scrubbed table.

Sister opened the three big cupboards. "Cooking stores. Cooking utensils, china and cutlery," she announced in turn.

"But nurses don't have to cook meals for the patients, do they?" Jean turned anxiously to Norah. "I thought you said the meals were sent, already cooked to the wards from the big kitchens of the hospital."

"Yes, they are," Norah assured her, "but we *do* cook a certain amount of invalid dishes in the little ward-kitchens. For instance, you'd never believe how many sorts of milk and fruit drinks there are to learn about . . . would she, Sister?"

"No, I don't suppose so. And, you see," Sister went on to explain, "the various sorts are suitable for various diseases, and the treatments of those diseases, so we aren't just out to *make* complications. They really are necessary.

"Besides, many of the smaller hospitals haven't dietetic kitchens in which to prepare the special diets which the doctor may order, so a nurse must know how to produce any diet that may be needed. She may require this knowledge for her final examinations, too."

"Is there anything a nurse *can't* do?" Jean asked in wonderment.

"There *may* be." Sister sounded doubtful. "But whatever it is, she'll find a way to fill the gap. Above all things a nurse must have common sense. If she hasn't, she'll either drop out of nursing within the first year, or find some other sense to take its place."

"Is that why they're supposed to be a bit bossy?" Jean wondered.

Norah chuckled. "Well, I'll be blowed! Have I been nursing a viper in my bosom all afternoon? Bossy indeed!"

Sister was laughing gaily.

A voice addressed them from the doorway. "I'm glad the tour is turning out to be a happy one."

"Matron!" gasped Norah in an undertone.

"I've come to see Sister, and I was directed by the sound of her laughter." Matron's voice was as soft as ever, but there was a warm note of amusement beneath its level tones.

"Perhaps Matron will be our judge," chuckled Sister. "Matron, the nursing profession stands accused of bossiness. . . ."

"No-no, I didn't say you *were*," Jean gasped in horror. "I-I only said you were *supposed* to be—I meant you *sometimes* are—oh dear." Poor Jean broke off, gulping in embarrassment.

But Matron was smiling, if a little sadly. "I hate to say it," she said slowly, "but it's true."

"Matron!" chorused Norah and Sister together.

"Well, isn't it? *Don't* look so hurt, Nurse," she laughed gently at Norah. "You don't have to be bossy if you'd sooner not be, but don't you think it's safer to admit that the demands our profession make upon us are inclined to encourage 'bossiness?' What made Jean pass that remark, anyhow?"

"Well, after seeing so many different things that Nurses are supposed to do," explained Jean, "I asked if there was anything they *couldn't* do."

"Exactly," nodded Matron. "And no doubt Sister told you that they did most things. Well, that's just my point. We know too much . . . and yet not quite enough. If I'm not careful I shall burst into platitudes, but it's all very difficult to explain. I know, I'll tell you a story.

"It happened to me when I was a young probationer at one of the big London hospitals. That was many years ago now. I had just got to the stage of feeling sure of myself, and this new confidence had gone to my head like wine.

"Daddy Bingham encouraged it. He was very old and very frightened of the pain in his broken leg. I'm not sure that he wasn't even more frightened of the frame and pulley with which we kept the leg in position. And he was certainly frightened of every one in uniform.

"So many fears made him very difficult to treat. Strangely enough I was the only person who could induce him to move an inch in his bed or eat a mouthful of food.

"It was through Daddy Bingham that I discovered this new power in myself; an airy matter-of-fact way of working my will on another person and even persuading them to like it.

"Unfortunately I was so proud of my new

accomplishment that I took it home with me, together with a certain intolerance for anyone who seemed less able to ‘ cope.’ As nurses we are *very* proud of our ability to cope, don’t you think so?

“Anyway, I had ideas about the way meals should be served, the way furniture should be cleaned, and the way all my relations should manage their lives. In a spirit of generosity—nurses usually *are* generous—I imparted these ideas at random. My mother was delighted to see me developing so many domestic instincts all at once, and advised me to put them *all* into practice when I had a home of my own.

“My father was even more instructive. He cornered me after I had ‘ turned-out ’ his pipe-rack. ‘ There now,’ said I, waving an airy hand over the stripped pipe-rack, ‘ *much* better, don’t you think so? There’s nothing more likely to infect a mouth than a dirty old pipe.’

“Then he let me have it.

“‘ I’ve chosen my own pipes, cleaned them and discarded them at my *own* will for the last forty years and I expect to be allowed to continue,’ he announced ungratefully. ‘ You, my child, have become a *managing* woman. That’s a pity, because people will avoid you. They will want to manage their own lives. My advice to you is this: Never try to work your will on another person unless you are sure it is necessary, and that every one will be the better for it. That, I am sure, will still give you every opportunity of *managing* your patients—who perhaps need it. And it will save ordinary people like myself from being stripped of our small dignities. Thanks, I'll have those pipes back.' Then he left me to digest the awful truth. I had grown bossy!

"I have often had to repeat that little lesson to myself since. It isn't easy when our work demands that we use a lot of personal persuasion, to forget it as soon as we leave the wards. Management becomes a habit . . . but *not* a habit to be encouraged."

Jean rather thought that Matron's last words were directed at Norah. Perhaps Norah *was* a bit bossy, but people seemed to love her to manage them. Jean tried to imagine a very much older Norah being very much more "managing" but gave up the effort as the little school-kitchen was invaded by three boisterous probationers.

They checked their noisy entrance as soon as they saw Matron and Sister.

The leader, a pretty girl with large intelligent eyes, arrested her movements on the instant, while the other two shuffled rather awkwardly behind. She stood poised like a crisp white butterfly and addressed Matron. "Please excuse us, but we came back to get our cookery books—we've left them in the cupboard."

Matron and Sister smiled their understanding

and the three figures glided silently across the room and out again with their three slim note-books.

"She walks like a dancer, doesn't she, Matron?" Sister's remark was more a statement than a question.

"Yes, beautifully. It's a pity, but perhaps she may find even greater expression in her new career. Who knows."

"Was she a dancer, then?" Jean asked with interest.

"Yes, she came to this hospital as a patient after falling down a flight of steps. She will never dance again. And when the doctor had told her so, she decided to become a nurse. So she has come to us."

"Do you often have people who have been other things first?" asked Jean.

"Yes, very often. At the moment we have an ex-schoolteacher, a nursery governess, a mannequin, a secretary—no, two secretaries, haven't we, Sister?"

"Yes, and an expert on beauty culture."

"That'll be Nurse Hunt, won't it?" Jean turned to Norah.

They both smiled at the recollection of Hunt and of her sea of mud.

"And we all mix-up very happily," finished Matron, triumphantly. "Well, Jean, have you enjoyed your afternoon?" she added as they all left the kitchen.

"Yes, I have *very* much," replied Jean truthfully.

"Good. Did she see everything, Nurse?" Matron inquired of Norah.

"Yes, I think so, Matron. I didn't take her to the surgical ward because they were operating this afternoon. But she saw inside the theatre after the operations were over; and, of course, she saw Mercy Ward and the Children's, and Out-patients'—and then on here. She even had a game of tennis, so she hasn't missed much," Norah finished laughingly.

Matron said good-bye at the entrance to the little school-wing, and she and Sister departed for their weekly report.

"Matron watches us from the very day we enter the P.T.S.," explained Norah as they sauntered towards the door of the Home. "She and Sister will enter into deep discussions about the possibilities of all the present set of pupils, so that when they come into the Hospital their careers can be most suitably shaped."

"Do they take so much trouble in every hospital?"

"No, not always, but as people become more and more interested in the nursing-service, so more care is taken of the way in which student nurses are trained. And, after all, it's up to every one to take the trouble to select a good hospital, just as their parents would select a good school."

"Yes, of course," Jean answered thoughtfully.

They had reached the wide stone steps on which Jean had stood not quite five hours before. "But it seems much longer," she said. "I've lived another life since then."

Norah laughed back at her. "And we'll expect you back again to see the tennis tournament."

Jean smiled her agreement. And as she turned to wave a last good-bye to Norah, her eyes rested for a moment on the warm, red brick of the Home. Even now through the wide open windows floated the sound of young voices, eager, laughing. They seemed to call her back.

And I may even come to stay one day, thought Jean happily. "See you soon," she called.

Her words floated through the summer air to where Norah stood with the sunlight on her crisp white apron.

THE END